MENDELSSOHN

THE INTERNATIONAL LIBRARY OF MUSIC

FOR HOME AND STUDIO

STUDY MATERIAL

IN TWO BOOKS

A Manual of Practical Instruction in Pianoforte Playing Combining
all the Essentials from the beginning of Grade
One through Grade Four

Compiled and Edited from the World's
Greatest Composers and Authorities

WITH ORIGINAL PIECES, TECHNICAL EXERCISES AND EXPLANATORY TEXT

BY

CHARLES DENNÉE

PROFESSOR OF PIANOFORTE PLAYING IN
THE NEW ENGLAND CONSERVATORY OF MUSIC
BOSTON, MASSACHUSETTS

VOLUME I

GRADES ONE AND TWO

1958

THE UNIVERSITY SOCIETY, INC.
Educational Publishers
NEW YORK

Copyright, 1955 by
THE UNIVERSITY SOCIETY
INCORPORATED

FOREWORD

IN THESE TWO VOLUMES it has been the aim of the publishers to assemble a complete equipment of study material to go into homes where children, or older persons, are either beginning the study of pianoforte playing, or are in the early or intermediate stages of advancement; one that will provide them with all the necessary technical exercises and studies, to carry them through the first four grades.

When Napoleon was congratulated on the achievement of a splendid victory, he replied sadly that another such victory would leave him without an army. A teacher of the piano who exacts from his students that which he deems best for the student's welfare and future progress, may achieve the victory of having his own way, but if this is gained at the expense of dulling the student's zest for his study, it is an empty victory. It is like one of those surgical operations which is perfectly successful—except the patient dies!

The other type of pedagogical strategist theorises that the maintaining of the student's interest is paramount to all else, and that even if progress be slower and less thorough, it at least must keep interest alive until a point is reached where a serious review can be safely undertaken to pick up the dropped stitches from the days when study was play instead of work.

These two phases of teaching are taken into consideration, but balanced in such a way that through the dark forest of technical struggle to the Fourth Grade, the young student is not confronted with studies which mean nothing more than hours of mechanical drudgery, for every effort has been directed toward making this particular work interesting through an appeal to the imagination, by titles, oftentimes based on the musical or rhythmical content of the study, and by the introduction of many well-known melodies.

The studies are all proven value through years of use by the best Conservatories and private teachers, and have been chosen and arranged to present a progressive and varied course of practice. By the use of this material one avoids the necessity for using a number of complete books by a few composers, in which there must necessarily be many studies that are superfluous, or that contain individual difficulties which render them impractical for consistent, steady progress. The studies are equally divided between the left hand, the right hand, and both hands. This avoids the usual undue development of the right hand, and tends to build a well-rounded capable technique in both hands.

The first grade material, selected from several well-known instruction books, is supplemented by original material and many interesting little pieces. The text has been compiled with a view of keeping before the pupil at all times, the important principles of fundamental training, providing a ready reference book to strengthen and assist the suggestions and the information that the teacher imparts from lesson to lesson.

The volumes have been compiled and edited by Mr. Charles Dennée, the well-known teacher and composer of Boston, whose reputation as one of our leading professors of the pianoforte is so well known that it needs no word of commendation from us. Mr. Dennée has been a member of the faculty at the New England Conservatory of Music since 1883.

In placing these volumes in the homes of the nation, the publishers feel that they are in a measure doing their part toward elevating the taste for good music. Aside from its practical purpose, this collection is one that will give enjoyment and satisfaction to many persons who play the piano and who wish a good selection of pieces for their own pleasure and that of their friends.

THE PUBLISHERS

TABLE OF CONTENTS

VOLUME I

GRADE I A

TABLE OF CONTENTS

GRADE II

TECHNICAL EXERCISES

STUDIES

TABLE OF CONTENTS

ix

PAGE

LIST OF GRADE I AND II COMPOSITIONS

CONTAINED IN THE INTERNATIONAL LIBRARY OF MUSIC

ARRANGED PROGRESSIVELY FROM THE EASIER TO THE MORE DIFFICULT.

GRADE I

GRADE II

LIST OF GRADE I AND II COMPOSITIONS

Elementary Exercises for Beginners

Compiled by Charles Dennée

ELEMENTS OF MUSIC

Musical notation is expressed by notes printed upon a staff consisting of five lines and four spaces, with added, or leger, lines above and below, to augment its scope.

The musical alphabet consists of seven letters: A, B, C, D, E, F, G.

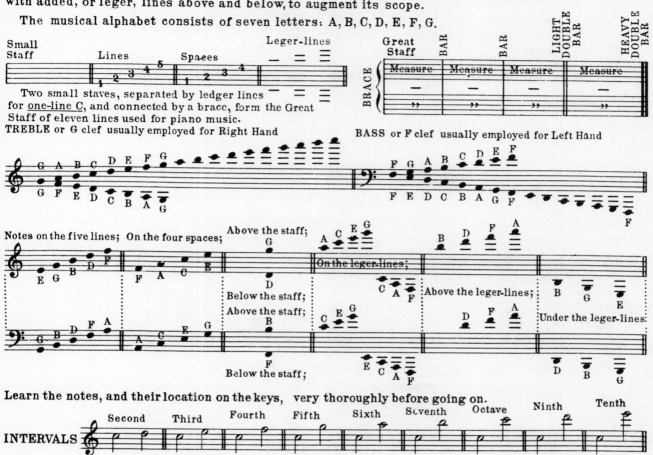

Two small staves, separated by ledger lines for one-line C, and connected by a brace, form the Great Staff of eleven lines used for piano music.

TREBLE or G clef usually employed for Right Hand

BASS or F clef usually employed for Left Hand

Learn the notes, and their location on the keys, very thoroughly before going on.

COMPARATIVE VALUE OF NOTES

Study these values very carefully before playing any exercises.

DOTTED NOTES

Value

DOTTED RESTS

Two Dots

Value

A dot always increases, by *one half,* the value of whatever precedes it, whether it be a note, dot or rest.

ACCIDENTALS, or CHROMATIC SIGNS

Sharp   Flat   Natural

C   C sharp   C natural   D   D flat   D natural

A sharp (♯) raises the pitch of a printed note a *half* step; literally, play next key above.

A flat (♭) lowers the pitch of a printed note a *half* step; literally, play next key below.

A natural (♮) restores a note to its original pitch, after it has been sharped or flatted.

A double sharp (♯♯ or ×) or a double flat (♭♭) indicates a *whole step* above, or below, printed note.

Names of the notes with sharps   Names of the notes with flats

C sharp D sharp E sharp F sharp G sharp A sharp B sharp C sharp   C flat D flat E flat F flat G flat A flat B flat C flat

CHROMATIC Write the scale with sharps, ascending; and with flats, descending.

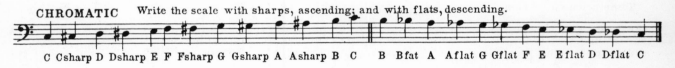

C C sharp D D sharp E F F sharp G G sharp A A sharp B C   B B fat A A flat G G flat F E E flat D D flat C

(✳) ENHARMONIC (the two possible ways of writing notes to be played upon the same key)

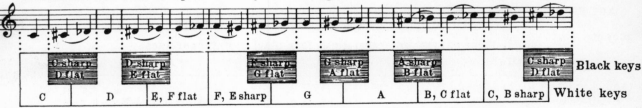

| | C sharp D flat | D sharp E flat | | F sharp G flat | G sharp A flat | A sharp B flat | | C sharp D flat | Black keys |
| C | | D | E, F flat | F, E sharp | G | | A | B, C flat | C, B sharp | White keys |

From one key to the *very next* key is a half step, (often called semi-tone.)
Twice this distance is a whole step; (from one key to the *2nd key above or below.*)

KEY SIGNATURES WITH TONIC TRIADS

C major A minor G major E minor D major B minor A major F♯ minor E major C♯ minor B major G♯ minor

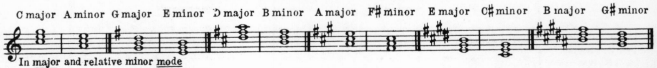

In **major** and relative minor **mode**

F major D minor B♭ major G minor E♭ major C minor A♭ major F minor D♭ major B♭ minor

Study all of these chords, until equally familiar with all keys. As broken triads, the tones played one after the other instead of together, they will be practised later on, after you have gained a knowledge of keys.

RHYTHM

TIME SIGNATURES SIMPLE COMPOUND

$\frac{12}{8}$ and $\frac{9}{8}$ rhythm is vitually the same as $\frac{4}{4}$ and $\frac{3}{4}$ rhythm with a triplet on each count.

(TRIPLE RHYTHM)

SIMPLE COMPOUND

The figures standing at the beginning of a composition, after the clefs and key signature, are called the Time Signature. The upper figure denotes the number of counts in a measure, the lower figure the value of the note that fills each count. e. g. $\frac{2}{4}$ means 2 counts, each count the value of a quarter note.

A HOLD ⌢ or PAUSE ⌢ indicates that whatever stands under, or over it, is held longer than the original value. This is a matter of taste but it should be held at least twice the value of the note or rest.

RHYTHM is a regular recurrence of accents, thus establishing a sense of regular pulsation in the flow of the musical thought or expression.

TIME is the subdivision of the measures into counts, or beats, of equal length. To keep time *count aloud,* carefully spacing the words, or counts, an equal distance apart.

Time without rhythm conveys no strong impression or sense to the ear, no matter how perfectly the length of the notes or counts are observed. The whole structure of music is built upon rhythm and accents, and this is as necessary in the practising of all exercises for the development of the fingers as it is in the performance of a composition.

ACCENT is special emphasis given to certain tones in playing. There are two kinds of accent, *natural* and *artificial.*

Natural accent falls upon the 1st and 3rd counts in $\frac{4}{4}$ rhythm, the 1st count in ordinary $\frac{3}{4}$ rhythm, (and $\frac{2}{4}$ rhythm), the 1st and 4th counts in $\frac{6}{8}$ rhythm, and in compound rhythms upon the notes where it would logically fall in the simple measures, or rhythms, from which compound rhythms are derived.

Artificial accent is special emphasis upon tones other than those which call for natural accent, and requires a special sign placed over or under a note to indicate that it is to receive this accent.

The signs of artificial accent are: > (ordinary accent), ∧, ∨, *sf*, *sfz*, or *fz*, *very strong* (explosive) *accents,* and — pressure accent. The sign ⊤ indicates a *pressure* accent in which the tone is not held quite the full value of the note *(non legato).*

4

LEGATO is imparting the *full* value to each note (or tone) thus producing a smooth, connected effect in playing a succession of tones. In other words each tone is to be sustained *until the next tone begins,* without the slightest break or detaching between them.

A SLUR ♪♪♪♪ is a curved line extending over two or more *different* notes. It is primarily an indication that all the notes under it are played legato, though it has further significance in marking the phrasing of a composition.

If a slur ends on the first note of a group, count or measure, that note is usually shortened in *held* value. Tied notes, dotted notes and half notes are an exception to this rule.

A SHORT SLUR occurs over *two* notes of different name and pitch. The first note receives an accent and the second is played softly and receives only one half its printed value, the other half of its value constituting rest, or silence.

EXAMPLES   Slur—not a tie.

Written: *Executed:*

If the last note of the slur has a dot over it, the note is to be very short; approximately one quarter of its printed value.

A TIE ♪♪ is a curved line connecting two *consecutive* notes, of the same name and pitch, into one continuous tone, the first note being played and the key held down *through* the full value of *both notes.* If either of the two notes has a dot over it the sign is a slur, not a tie, and both notes are played.

REPEAT MARKS — Two dots standing before a double bar indicate a repetition of the composition from the beginning; ex. 𝄇 But, if this is preceded by another double bar with dots *after* it, the repetition begins from this point instead of the beginning; ex. 𝄆 𝄇

8va ...., or *8* ------- placed over notes indicates that these notes are to be played an octave higher than they are written.

8va bassa placed under the staff indicates that the notes over it are to be played an octave lower.

Con 8. indicates that *an octave* is to be played instead of a single note; the thumb playing the printed note and the little finger *(simultaneously)* its octave.

D. C., Da Capo, or *D.C. al Fine,* placed at the end of a composition or movement, indicates that the player should go back to the beginning and play the composition through again to the word *Fine,* or the sign ⌒ placed over a double bar, both of which indicate the close or finish.

D. S., or *Dal Segno* means return to the sign 𝄋 and play through to the end of the composition as indicated by the word *Fine* or the sign ⌒ over a double bar.

TRIPLETS

A TRIPLET is a group of three notes with an italic (or *slanting*)figure *3* over or under it. In such a case the three notes are played in the value of *two similar notes.* Ex. ♩♩♩ are played in the value of 𝅗𝅥 or ♩ ♩, and ♪♪♪ are played in the value of ♩ or ♪♪

In playing triplets the first note should receive a slight accent. If an entire movement, or passage, is in triplets, the figure *3* is sometimes written over the first measure groups only, it being understood thereby that the following groups are triplets.

This form of writing comes under the head of artificial grouping. There are other forms of artificial grouping, ♪♪♪♪♪ , ♪♪♪♪♪♪ , ♪♪♪♪♪♪♪ etc., the performance of which is generally obvious.

MARKS USED TO INDICATE DEGREES OF FORCE

p – (piano) soft;— *pp – (pianissimo)* extremely soft;— *mf – (mezzoforte)* moderately loud;— *mp – (mezzopiano)* louder than *p,* softer than *mf;* — *f – (forte)* loud;— *ff – (fortissimo)* extremely loud.

SIGNS FOR VARYING EFFECTS OF THE ABOVE MARKS

Crescendo *(cresc.)* — gradually increase the force; also indicated by this sign: ‹———

Diminuendo *(dim.)* — gradually decrease the force; also indicated by this sign: ———›

A Swell, or combined *cresc.* and *dim.,* is indicated thus: ‹——— ———›

For further instruction in signs and marks of speed etc. study the table given at the end of the *Grade.*

THE KEYBOARD OF A MODERN 7⅓ OCTAVE PIANOFORTE

Showing the staff notation for each white key, and the subdivision of the keyboard into groups (sometimes called octaves)

The letters show the manner of marking names of notes in each group if desired

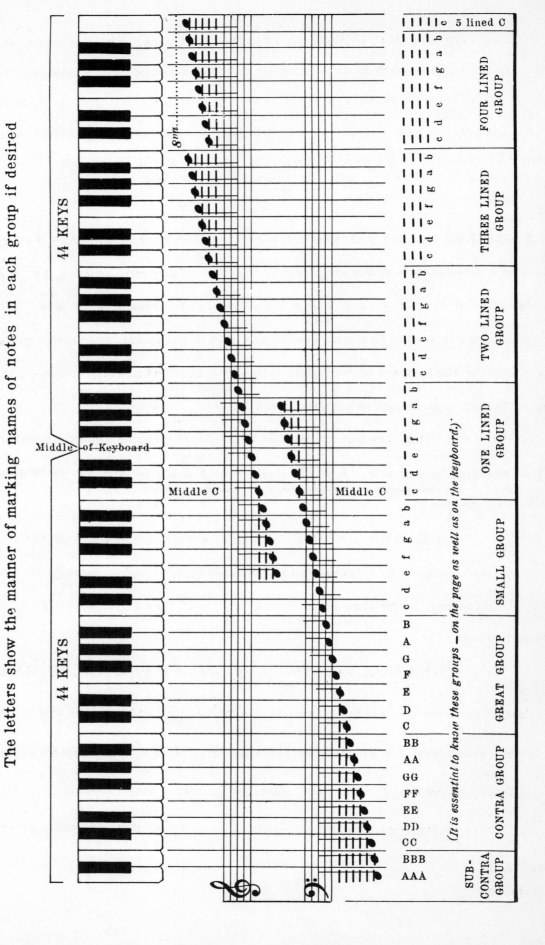

POSITION AT THE PIANOFORTE

The player should sit upon a chair *(preferably)* or stool, high enough to bring the elbows on a horizontal line with the tops of the white keys. The elbows should be a trifle in front of the front line of the body. The wrist should be *slightly* lower than the knuckles and the fingers curved so that they strike upon the cushion at the end of each finger; the palm of the hand slightly arched. The knuckles will then be *slightly* raised; they should never be depressed, nor should they be pushed or forced up to an awkward or pronounced elevation in playing the fingers.

The fingers should *lift from the knuckle joint*, and play with a quick, easy stroke, moving on the knuckle, without any assistance from the hand or arm.

The muscles of the arm should be supple,(as should the wrist) but always *supported,* and never allowed to drag or pull upon the keys.

The unoccupied *(or non-playing)* fingers should be kept lifted while any one finger is holding a key, and *that* finger should be immediately lifted up into the position of the other fingers the instant it releases a key, this occurring as a new key is struck by another finger, or at a rest. These conditions are modified in many cases by the requirements of more advanced playing, but are imperative throughout the early stages of development.

Never stiffen or strain the muscles, and do not attempt force or power until the fingers are under full control, in easy, free motions at a moderate degree of force, even though the tone is only piano or pianissimo at first.

THE USE OF TREBLE AND BASS CLEFS

The editor can not agree with those methods or instruction books in which the use of the Bass Clef is delayed. Common sense would seem to dictate the association of the Bass Clef with the left hand from the very beginning of study, as this clef predominates in all music for the notation of the lower, or left hand staff.

The use of the Treble Clef in the left hand is an exception to the rule, as is the use of the Bass Clef for the right hand. Both exceptions occur frequently, but the fundamental principle stated above is necessary to avoid confusion. If the left hand starts playing from Treble Clef notation it is a difficult task to change later to the Bass Clef, and the pupil is puzzled and confused as a result of this. In such instances it is unlearning something which has become fixed in the mind, by practice and association, and substituting a new method of reading. This is much more difficult than it is to learn and practise the Bass Clef from the very first.

NOTE-WRITING PRACTICE

The pupil should procure a music blank book and spend considerable time each day writing notes and rests of different values, with the names written over them. Also write the seven letters of the musical alphabet in every conceivable order and then place the proper note under each letter, both on the staff and on leger lines above and below.

This writing practice is invaluable for becoming thoroughly familiar with the notes and their values. The teacher should provide examples in both letters and notes.

8

THE IMPORTANCE OF REVIEW WORK

The material contained in the early pages of Grade I is a foundation for all future musical knowledge. If the pupil continues the study of each point until it is mastered, the final result will be excellence. If the pages are so skimmed through as to leave a doubt as to their meaning, the outcome will be inferiority.

The only way by which young musicians can get a firm grasp on these elementary principles, is by constantly reviewing what has been studied.

Special emphasis should be laid upon a knowledge of note values, time, rhythm, and note locations on the staff, with a positive knowledge of the piano keys upon which they should be played.

ROBERT SCHUMANN'S RULES FOR YOUNG MUSICIANS

The most important thing is to cultivate the Sense of Hearing. Take pains early to distinguish Tones and Keys by the ear. The bell, the window-pane, the cuckoo—seek to find what tones they each give out.

You must diligently practise Scales and other finger exercises. But there are many persons who imagine all will be accomplished if they keep on spending many hours each day, till they grow old, in mere mechanical practice. It is about as if one should busy himself daily with repeating the A-B-Cs as fast as possible, and always faster and faster. Use your time better.

Strive to play easy pieces well and beautifully. It is better than to render more difficult pieces only indifferently well.

You must not only be able to play your little pieces with the fingers; you must be able to hum them over without a piano. Sharpen your imagination so that you may fix in your mind not only the Melody of a composition, but also the Harmony belonging to it.

Accustom yourself, even though you have but little voice, to sing at sight without the aid of an instrument. The sharpness of your hearing will continually improve by that means. But if you are the possessor of a rich voice lose not a moment's time, but cultivate it and consider it the fairest gift which heaven has lent you.

You must gradually make acquaintance with all the more important works of all the important masters.

If you can find out little melodies for yourself on the piano it is all very well. But if they come of themselves when you are not at the piano, then you have still greater reason to rejoice; for then the inner sense of music is astir in you. The fingers must make what the head wills, not *vice versa*.

Listen attentively to all songs of the people; they are a mine of the most beautiful melodies and open for you glimpses into the character of different nations.

The study of the History of Music, supported by the actual hearing of the master compositions of the different epochs, is the shortest way to cure you of self-esteem and vanity.

Dragging and hurrying are equally great faults.

Without enthusiasm nothing real comes of art.

There is no end of learning.

EXERCISES FOR FINGER DEVELOPMENT AND CONTROL

Practise very slowly and strictly observe the correct and precise motions of the fingers. Be sure that the fingers are kept curved at all times, never allow them to straighten out or curl in when they lift.

WHOLE NOTES

Right Hand
Count four to each whole note.   *Left Hand*

The fingers are numbered 1 2 3 4 5, the thumb is 1 and the little finger is 5. Repeat these exercises with the fingers in the same five-key position, but beginning on D, E, F, G, A and B. This is simple transposition.

Right Hand

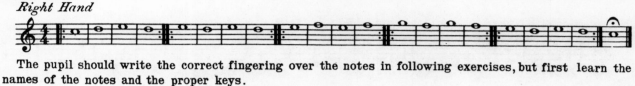

The pupil should write the correct fingering over the notes in following exercises, but first learn the names of the notes and the proper keys.

Left Hand

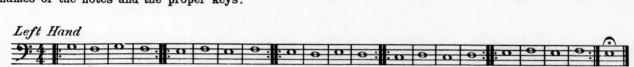

R.H.

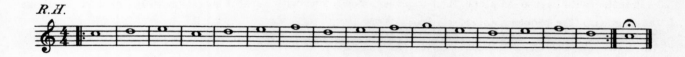

L.H.

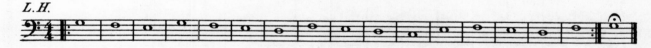

HALF NOTES

R.H.
Count four in each measure, two to each half note.

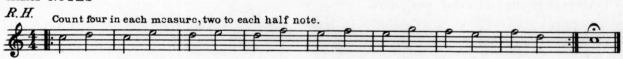

L.H.

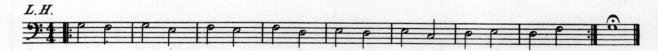

HALF NOTES AND WHOLE NOTES

R.H. Observe the note values, and give the correct number of counts to each note.

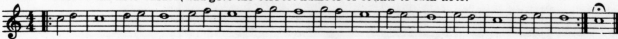

L.H.

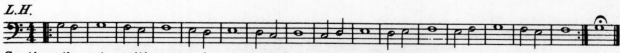

Continue the note-writing exercises, using whole notes and half notes.

LEGER LINES BELOW THE STAFF
for the right hand.

PLAYING THE HANDS TOGETHER

The following pages present considerable apparent repetitions in the general character of the exercises, but this is necessary, to ensure correct reading and the thorough adjustment of the fingers to the keys, before going on to the more difficult part of the grade.

Practise with each hand alone, then together, slowly and with careful attention to lifting and striking the fingers in the proper manner.

Count aloud, 4 equal counts to each measure. Write the fingering.

Transpose to other five-key positions.

LITTLE STUDIES BUILT ON SLOW TRILLS
Introducing the use of Ties

Very Slow — Moderate — A Little Faster.   Write the fingering.

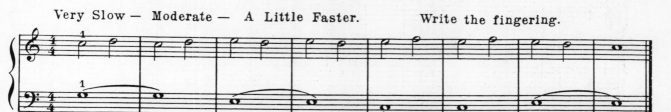

Set the metronome at 44— then 52, and finally at 60.   One metronome click to each count; four clicks to a measure.

M. M. = 44 - 52 - 60

SIMPLE IMITATION
Introducing the use of Rests

M. M. = 44 - 52 - 60

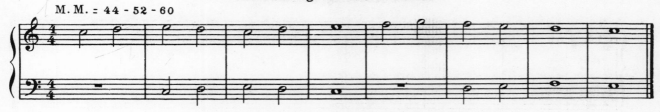

SIMPLE FORM OF SYNCOPATION
using Ties

Syncopation results from the delaying, or transferring of the accent from its natural place in the measure, to a count that is usually weak, or otherwise unaccented.

M. M. = 44 - 52 - 60

SLOW TRILLS IN CONTRARY MOTION

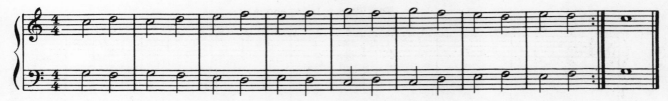

When these studies are learned, repeat them in $\frac{2}{2}$ rhythm, using two counts to a measure instead of four. If the metronome continues at the same speed as before, the study will be played twice as fast as when four counts were used. Thus the metronome gives one beat for each half note, and two beats for each whole note.

STUDIES IN CONTRARY MOTION

Escríbase la correcta digitación

Write the proper fingering

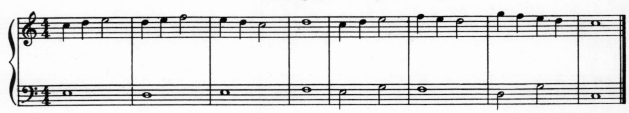

STUDY IN RHYTHM

Introducing Quarter Notes

STUDY IN PARALLEL MOTION

(En un movimiento moderado)

Moderato *(at a moderate speed)*

STUDIES IN CONTRARY AND PARALLEL MOTION

For Finger Independence

Moderato

10-735-60

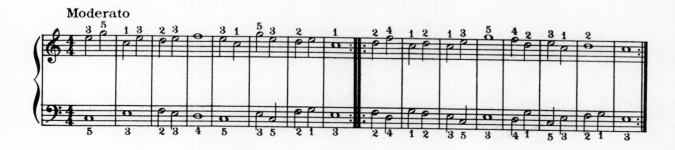

FIVE FINGERS TAKE A STROLL

LEFT HAND FOLLOWS THE RIGHT

TWO MELODIOUS PIECES
For Four Hands

ANTON DIABELLI

For reading practice the pupils part is written for both hands in the treble clef.

What is the meaning of 𝄞·········? Or as sometimes written 8ᵛᵃ··········?

2-744-52

ANTON DIABELLI

Andante cantabile

Pupil

Teacher

Andante cantabile

16

Moderato   **UP AND DOWN THE PIAZZA STEPS**
Write in the correct fingering. Notice the dotted notes and use of the tie.

Find the definition of new terms and signs before playing each new exercise or piece. What are repeat signs, and their purpose?

Moderato   **A GOOD RESOLVE**   CHARLES DENNÉE

Name the intervals in each piece.

STUDY IN INTERVALS

Allegretto *(brightly and cheerfully; not too fast)* *(Brillante y alegre; no muy ligero)*

What is the meaning of a dot following a note? of this sign 𝄽 ? How many do you count for a dotted half-note?

Study definition for *D.C. al Fine*   Estúdiese el significado de: *D. C. al Fine*
12-735-60

STUDY IN CONTRARY MOTION

Introducing Dotted Notes
For practise in playing the left hand part in the treble clef.

LEFT HAND IMITATES THE RIGHT

CHARLES DENNÉE

MY FIRST WALTZ

CHARLES DENNÉE

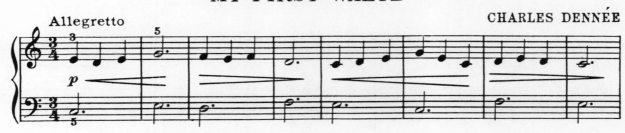

HOMEWARD BOUND

BEYER

PUPIL

TEACHER

SLOW WALTZ

BEYER

PUPIL

TEACHER

PRIMARY SCHOOL MARCH

PUPIL

BEYER

TEACHER

Moderato

These contain all intervals up to and including a Fifth. Remember the effect of the long slurs? What is the effect when the slur ends on a half or whole note?

Transpose to begin on A, B, G, D and E. Why does the lowering of the pitch change the character?

Transpose downward to begin on G; also on A. What changes are required in these keys.

Name all the notes and intervals, and the keyboard groups to which they belong. Then write these group names under all the note groups in the preceding pieces.

LEGER LINES ABOVE THE STAFF
(IN THE BASS CLEF)

LEFT HAND

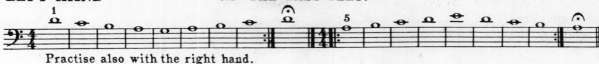

Practise also with the right hand.

Practise the notes on leger lines until they are as easy to read as those within the staff.

LEGER LINES BELOW THE STAFF

LITTLE RECREATIONS IN NOTE VALUES

Allegro moderato *(moderately fast)*   CHARLES DENNÉE

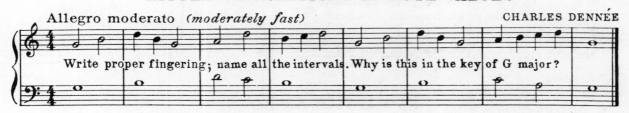

Write proper fingering; name all the intervals. Why is this in the key of G major?

Allegro moderato

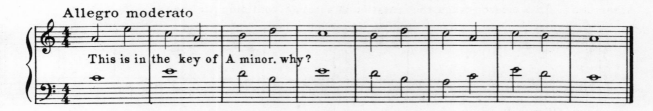

This is in the key of A minor. why?

THE LEFT HAND EXPLORES THE UPPER REGION

Allegretto

Name the notes and intervals, and the keyboard groups to which they belong.

THE LEFT HAND GAINS COURAGE

Allegretto

PUSSY CAT AT PLAY

Allegretto

See the pret-ty pus - -sy, play-ing in the sun, when

Explain effect of a dot after a note.

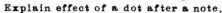

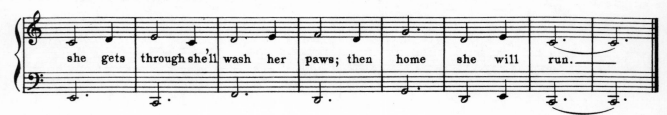

she gets through she'll wash her paws; then home she will run.

Answering Voices

Moderato

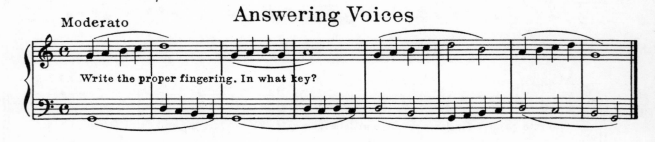

Write the proper fingering. In what key?

Two Little Canons

PERFECT CANON

Canon is the imitation (or reproduction) in one hand, of what has previously been played in the other hand. In a perfect canon the imitation is absolute, continuing to the end.

(Whole Rest)

IMPERFECT CANON

In an imperfect canon the ending is changed to permit the voices to finish together.

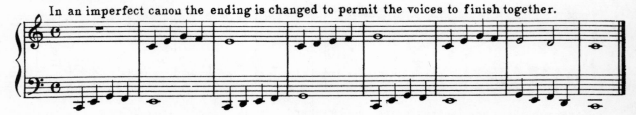

16-735-60

THEME AND VARIATIONS

HUMMEL

Morning Recreation

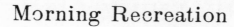

Moderato

Write fingering for all the notes

The Daily Round

Moderato

Song of the Toiler

Note the use of the tie

Allegretto

This piece uses the first five tones of the scale of G major

Plaintive Mood

CHARLES DENNÉE

Moderato con espressione (*With expression*)

This piece is in D minor

A Little Song

Moderato (*Con espressione*)

Observe the signs indicating *crescendo* and *diminuendo*

Country Boy's Song

Moderato (*but jolly*)

A Merry Roundelay

Allegretto (*Bright and cheerful*)

legato

FINGER EXERCISES IN 8th NOTES

Play slowly at first - Hands separate until sureness is gained

Count four, two 8th notes to each count

A CONTINUOUS PASSAGE FOR THE FIVE FINGERS

20-735-60

Transpose to five-finger positions beginning on G, D, A, E and F. Study the table of Key Signatures to find which notes are Sharp or Flat in each of these five-finger positions.

Learn the names of these notes, their location upon the keyboard and the name of the "Key-group or Octave," (see diagram of keyboard) before proceeding to the following pages. This is imperative, in order to recognize the notes, and find them upon the keyboard, without halting or puzzling over them when learning the following exercises and pieces.

Right Hand   Name the notes aloud at first

Graceful Dance

C. FREDRIC

Observe rests and signs for swell, also notation in Treble Clef for left hand

Allegretto

Write the proper fingering.

Fairy March

C. FREDRIC

Allegro moderato *(moderately fast)*

Notice crescendo sign.   Accent 1st and 3rd counts of each measure. By supplying an accompaniment the teacher may make duets of these two pieces.

Compare the notes in the G clef, with those in the F clef, which are played on the same keys.

What is the other name for G clef; for F clef?

For rhythmic practise and the development of facility

The following exercises should be practised with both hands together after they are well learned separately. Play slowly, with accurate lift and stroke of the fingers, keeping them curved at all times.

Count 4 equal counts in each measure

Practise and learn but *one* exercise at a time; do not try several at once.

Also transpose to the keys of D, A and F, and eventually to every scale beginning on a white key.

18-735-60

Three Little Duets
(Two players, 4 hands)

Teacher's Part

Secondo
(2nd, or lower part)

F. BEYER

Three Little Duets

For reading leger line notes above the treble staff

Pupil's Part

Primo

(1st, or upper part)

F. BEYER

FOR THE STUDY OF TRILLS AND INTERVALS

A FLUTE SOLO

MOFFET

A BASSOON SOLO

MOFFET

Theme and Variations

A. E. MÜLLER

Allegro moderato

For the application of previous exercises. Of what are these musical figures composed?

Illustrating the use of the tie and dotted notes; also of broken chords.

Maypole Dance

Allegretto

Notice 8th rests

19-735-60

TRAINING IN RHYTHM

Rhythm is the most important element in music. Perfect rhythm is possible only when one understands and feels the constant repetitions of accent at regular intervals. Persistent training is the only way to establish this habit in the minds of young piano pupils.

Of the ways in which one can be taught to feel these rhythmic impulses, the following are of value: Marching to a strongly accented march, played by the teacher. Dancing to the different primary rhythms. Clapping of the hands or drumming upon a table, using both hands. Listening to the ticking of a clock, to the ringing of bells, to bands or street pianos, or similar *regularly accented* sounds. The metronome teaches *strict time*, but it cannot teach rhythm, *since all its beats have the same force. Rhythm is time with the addition of accents!*

ATTRACTIVE RECREATION FOR CHILDREN

The child mind becomes dull, and interest lags unless attractive material is provided to offset the tedious practice of exercises, and the necessary study of purely technical terms and the fundamentals of music.

Keen interest can be created by giving to children something that appeals to their natural instincts. Nothing so quickly and so surely establishes a sense of time and rhythm as the association of rhymes with tunes that are easily remembered. By these means the natural swing of the words is associated with the rhythm of the music, the pupil absorbing the fundamentals of time and rhythm in a natural way. Marching or beating time to such melodies also is helpful.

ORAL ACCENT OR IMPULSE TRAINING

Oral training should be applied to all words, before the teacher plays the notes. For example:

The *large heavy* syllables are spoken in a loud voice; the *small heavy* ones, only moderately loud; the *small light* ones softly. When the words are repeated rapidly, only the large heavy syllables are accented. Repeat the words aloud many times; then repeat them while playing the notes; thirdly, sing the tune to the words, with and without playing; also play the notes, and *think the words;* finally, sing and play together.

LITTLE JACK HORNER

LIT	tle	Jack	HOR	—	ner	SAT	in	a	COR	—	ner	
EAT	ing	a	CHRIST	—	mas	Pie	—	—	—	—	; He	
STUCK	in	his	THUMB	—	and	PULLED	out	a	PLUM	—	and	
SAID	what	a	GREAT	boy	am	I	—	—	—	—	—	

Apply this oral model to the other song exercises. In "London Bridge," accent the words or syllables which fall upon the first and third counts, the first count slightly louder than the third. The same applies to "Taps." In "The Little Lost Dog," the first count in each measure is emphasized, the other syllables or words following smoothly and easily. "Old Black Joe" is accented the same as "London Bridge," but as it is slower, the emphasis is less strong.

Other rhythmic exercises may be formed by applying the principles of the oral model to well known nursery rhymes, simple hymns and songs. By repeating the words in a natural way, you will be enabled to place the accents in their proper positions. The accents may then be slightly exaggerated, as previously suggested.

Nursery Rhymes And Bed-Time Stories

Unaccompanied melodies, for imparting rhythmic swing and quick perception of note values, through the medium of word association.

Refer back to these song melodies while pursuing the material on the following ten pages.

Little Jack Horner

In Triple Rhythm

Observe the B-flat. What is the meaning, and in which Key or scale does it place this melody?

London Bridge

Observe the F-sharp. Where is it played? What is the meaning? In what "Key" is the melody written?

The Little Oboe and the Big Trombone

What is the meaning of the lines under the notes? of the letters *p* and *f*?

When these songs can be played with the right hand, repeat them also with the left hand.

A MELODY DIVIDED BETWEEN THE HANDS

The following melodies extend beyond the compass of a five finger position and the two hands are used alternately in playing them.

TAPS

This bugle call commands that all lights be turned out in a fort, or any army camp. It is also played at the end of a burial service for a soldier.

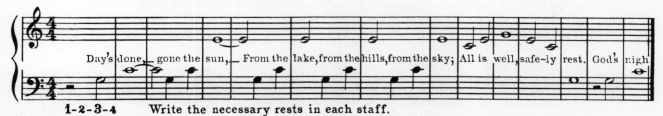

1-2-3-4   Write the necessary rests in each staff.

34

The Little Lost Dog

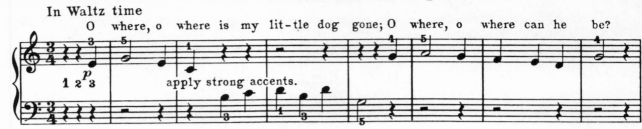

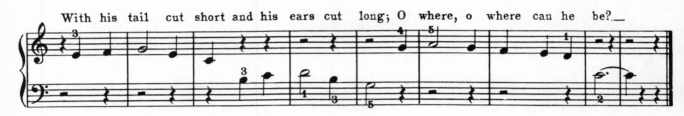

A FAMILIAR OLD SONG

Old Black Joe
Plantation Melody

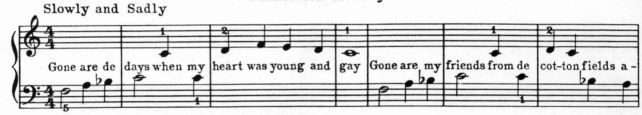

The pupil should insert the missing rests.

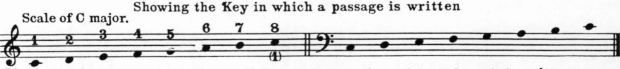

What kind of rests are missing? What "Key"or scale requires a flat on B, with all the other notes played on white keys? How many counts to each half note? to each quarter rest? When should a note before a rest be released? Where does any count end?

Scale Models
Showing the Key in which a passage is written

Scale of C major.

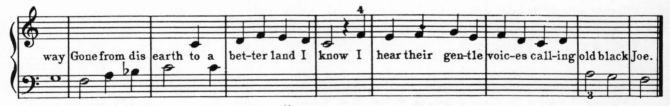

The lines and spaces on the staff are called *staff degrees*. As each tone of a scale is written on a different staff degree, the scale notes may be called *scale degrees*. This major scale begins and ends on C, and music which is based on this scale is said to be in the Key of C major.

Scale of G major, ascending.

F-sharp as an accidental   First five notes   Last five notes   The sharp included in the signature

7-744-52

Changing The Key— Modulation

The addition of the *sharp* on F changes the Key from C to G major

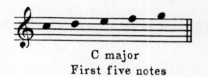 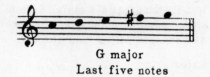

C major
First five notes

G major
Last five notes

Modulation illustrated by the use of accidentals.

Begins in C major   Changes to G major

Then returns to C major

The eighth measure ending in G major leaves us with the feeling that it would be unfinished, if left in that condition. In the ninth measure, it returns to the Key in which the piece began, which gives us a sense of satisfaction. The sixteen measures form a short but complete musical composition.

Modulation illustrated by the use of key signatures.

C major   G major

Continue the repetition of the first four measures

The Key of G major, without Key signature or accidentals.

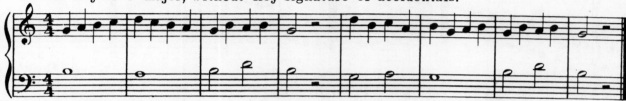

Although in the Key of G major, the note F happens not to be used, hence neither key signature nor accidental is required. Many pieces in Grade 1 are so written; study each one to decide in what key it is.

ELEMENTARY "KEY" ANALYSIS

In examples within a five-finger compass

Scale degrees consist of whole-steps and half-steps; hence such scales are termed diatonic scales.

In the first five degrees of a major diatonic scale, the half step is between the third and forth tones; in a minor diatonic scale it is between the second and third tones. In all ascending scales there is a half step between the seventh degree and the octave.

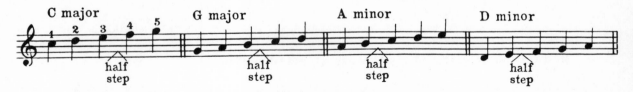

The first of the examples is in the Key of C major, even though it begins on F, as can be seen by the location of the half-step. In the Key of F major, the B must be altered by a flat. A flat also on A produces the first five degrees of the Key of F minor.

STUDY FOR SCALE FORMING

Four-Finger Exercise

This study in scale passages with alternating hands is for the acquirement of equality and independence of hands and fingers. It also teaches fluency and smoothness in joining passages for separate hands into one continuously flowing passage, or run. There should be no break in passing from one hand to the other.

This study also illustrates the two ways of writing the left hand part. When the notes go too high above the staff to be written on leger lines, they may be written on the treble staff above, with stems turned down, or a treble clef may be written on the lower staff.

Learn each two-measure section thoroughly before going on to the next; then play straight through without repeats.

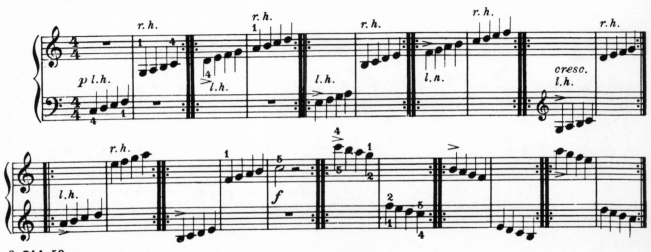

The entire exercise is in the **Key of C major**, the scale passages beginning on different scale-degrees. This is proved by the fact that all the half-steps lie between E and F, and B and C,—the third and fourth, and seventh and eighth scale degrees, of the Key of C major.

SIMPLE BROKEN THIRDS
In five-finger position

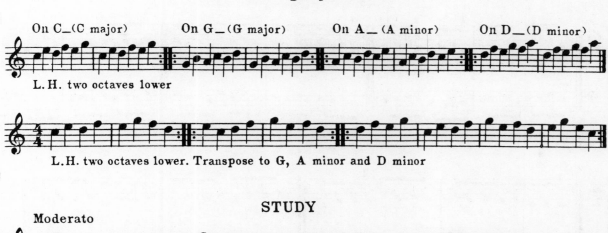

L.H. two octaves lower

L.H. two octaves lower. Transpose to G, A minor and D minor

STUDY

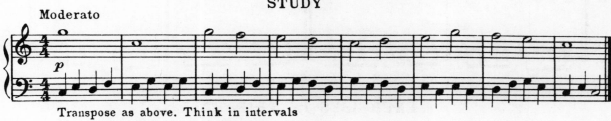

Transpose as above. Think in intervals

BROKEN THIRDS IN TRIPLE RHYTHM

A TWISTER

Finger Exercises

For devoloping skill in playing of broken figures

Repeat each passage 20 times

Practise *slowly*, paying strict attention to the fingers

Continue practising these exercises *daily*. Transpose also to G, D, A, E and F.

EXERCISES IN TRIPLETS

A slight emphasis on the first tone of each Triplet

Descriptive Pieces
On five — finger positions
UP THE LADDER AND DOWN THE LADDER

CHARLES DENNÉE

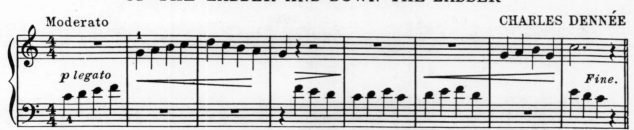

The first four measures form the ascending, and descending scale of C major.

Answering Echoes
PERFECT CANON

Transpose to five finger position on G.

Tagging
IMPERFECT CANON

Transpose to G major;

FUNDAMENTAL BROKEN TRIADS

Triads are formed by placing one Interval of a third above another

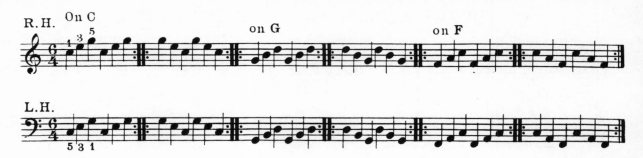

ELABORATED BROKEN TRIADS

Apply also to triads on F and G. Observe how each exercise consists of two broken thirds. When learned with the hands separately, play with both hands together; with repeats, then without.

IN GRACEFUL CURVES

Containing simple broken triads. An arpeggio is the repetition of a broken chord, through a higher or lower octave or octaves, forming one continuous passage. Confirm: Key *A minor*; Time signature, three-eighth; tempo indication, *moderato*.

Round We Go

Study in dotted notes; application of broken triads

Allegro moderato *(moderately fast)*

F. BEYER

Dolly's First Waltz

C. FREDRIC

Allegretto.

mf grazioso (gracefully)

Study the signs of force and accent very carefully.

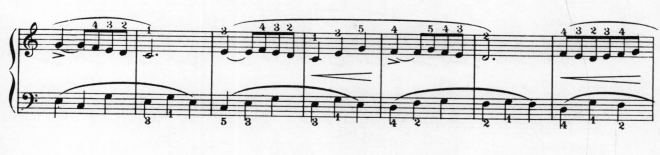

25-735-60

42

Simple Expansion
Exercises for extending the hand beyond the five finger position.

Continue practising the above exercises throughout the First Grade.

Keep the fingers curved and avoid straining or motions of any sort with the hand or arm. Play with easy, flexible muscles and do not stiffen the knuckles. Later on, in the Second Grade, transpose these exercises to other keys.

The Whistling Farmer Boy

F. BEYER

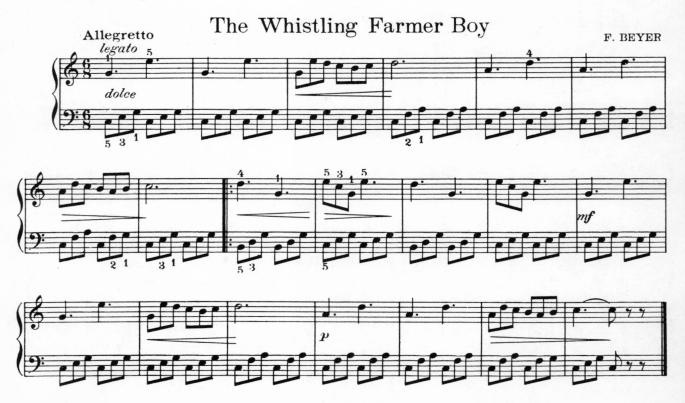

REPEATING A KEY WITH THE SAME FINGER

This should not be attempted until considerable control has been attained in playing the fingers in both regular and alternate succession on different keys. Repeating the same key in the first weeks of study is likely to induce "jumping" or "pumping," and thus prevent the acquirement of a smooth, easy, finger *legato*. For this reason the pupil thus far in this book has been confined to exercises which do not require any form of note repetition

To play the repeated note in these exercises, hold each key until it is time to play the next note. Then release the pressure of the finger enough to let the key up, and quickly, but easily, *press* the key down again with the same finger.

This touch should be conscientiously drilled; it is important. When a heavy tone is desired, the hand assists by imparting its weight to the pressure of the finger. For the present, keep the tip of the finger against the surface of the key.

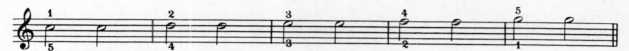

Play the left hand two octaves lower. Use fingering under notes.

FIRST ATTEMPT AT SPEED

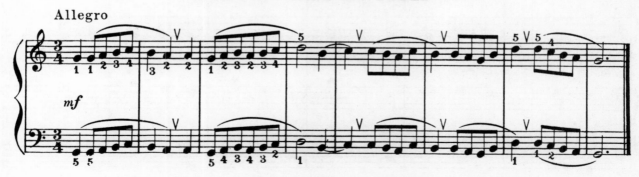

THE RAIN IS FALLING

(Duet for two players of equal skill)

BEYER

Rain drops

45

y

b

MELODIOUS STUDIES
Built on five finger Exercises
Combining half-notes, quarter-notes and eighth-notes

DIATONIC FINGER PASSAGES AND SIMPLE BROKEN TRIADS

VARIED NOTE VALUES AND INTERVALS

A LITTLE SONG
Applying repetition of the same key

Moderato

C. FREDRIC

STUDY IN ELEMENTARY EXPANSION

Moderato

LOESCHHORN

In what Key? Why?

In what Key?

15-744-52

FINGER EXERCISES IN 8th NOTES

Simple transposition; play the left hand an octave lower using fingering under notes.

Repeat each passage 8 times very slowly, observing rule for finger action.

Observe rule for accenting triplets. The slanting figure *3* denotes triplets, not fingering.

EXERCISES FOR ELEMENTARY HARMONY AND ARPEGGIOS
(Also for the study of triplets)

To make all the fingers of both hands of equal strength and independence, practise the above exercises with each hand alone and then with both together. Always be careful that the touch is not constrained in any way. Particularly see that the hands are held well over the keys, that the fingers act promptly both in striking and lifting.

Two Short Pieces
Morning Salute
Melody with broken triad accompaniment

Allegro

Happy Song
Study the triple rhythm, the time signature, dotted notes and the meaning of the various terms employed.

50

THE HANDS GO TRAVELING
A Trip to the Land of G major

CHARLES DENNÉE

Andantino   Make the melody sing.

AN EVENING BARCAROLLE
In the Harbor of D major

Moderato In each hand the third finger plays a sharped note

THE HANDS MAKE A TOUR IN A MAJOR

DANCING IN A FOREIGN LAND
To a tune in E major
In each hand the third finger plays G sharp

Allegretto

HOMEWARD BOUND
Through F major

Allegretto Make the melody sweet and singing

Hippety-Hop

H. BERENS, Op. 70

One count to a measure if played fast

Little Puzzle

Name the notes on the leger lines above the bass clef staff.

Name the left hand notes.

A Basket Full

Including all of the note values studied thus far.

A. LOESCHHORN

52

JIG
GIGUE

PUPIL

FRENCH FOLK SONG

THE FIRST ANTIPHONAL

THE SECOND ANTIPHONAL

FINGER EXERCISES IN DIFFERENT RHYTHMIC GROUPINGS

Dotted Quarters and Eighths.

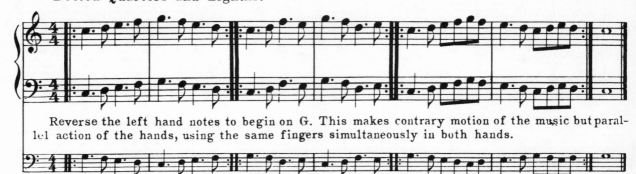

Reverse the left hand notes to begin on G. This makes contrary motion of the music but parallel action of the hands, using the same fingers simultaneously in both hands.

Dotted Eighths and Sixteenths. Observe the time value of the sixteenth note, and its proportionate size as compared to the remainder of the count.

Also with the Left Hand part reversed; parallel fingering— contrary motion.

Apply also to Triplets

Triplet Variant

Practice the Triplet rhythm until it is easy to play each exercise in each rhythm. Also alternate the rhythms in successive measures; then on successive counts. Copy some of the earlier exercises and pieces, using these rhythms, and practise until freedom is established in the playing of the dotted groups.

REVIEW AND MEMORIZING

A general review of all the preceding work should be made to attain fluency and speed in the more important technical exercises and in a few of the more pleasing pieces, many of which the pupil should by this time be able to play from memory. The memorizing of a certain number of pieces should be insistently required, as this enables the pupil to give more thought to the manner of playing and the effects to be produced.

EXAMINATIONS

A thorough examination should be given covering all the Elements of music taught in the beginning of piano study. Special emphasis should be placed upon note values and their equivalent groupings into notes of smaller value; upon time and rhythm; the meaning of the signs; the location of notes in the different keyboard groups. Frequent examinations are desirable to prevent the pupil from becoming forgetful or careless.

Staccato

Staccato is shortening the value of the note by releasing the key before the full value has expired; this is done in single tones by simply releasing the key with the finger.

In double notes the keys are released by lifting the hand easily and gracefully from the wrist.

In a continuous succession of staccato notes play from the wrist, lifting the hand for the silence (or rest) and bringing it down with a quick easy movement for the keys; hold the fingers and hand in shape and do not lift or strike with the fingers. In continuous successions of staccato notes lift the hand before playing the first note to gain equality and precision in the motions.

Staccato is indicated by dots placed over, or under, the notes, or by the word *staccato*.

The dot over a note reduces its *held value* one half.

EXAMPLE: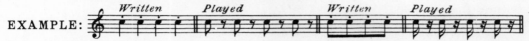

A sharp point or dash over a note reduces the *held value* three quarters, and is called *staccatissimo*.

EXAMPLE:

There is another form called portamento, written with both dots and slurs over the notes. This reduces the *held value* of the notes one quarter, sometimes less in slow tempos.

Portamento is a *pressure touch,* the keys are pressed down and released in an easy graceful manner. This touch calls for special illustration and training by the teacher. It is essentially smooth in character, and nice quality of tone is the thing to be most sought for.

EXAMPLE:

Slow or widely detached single staccato notes are played with a pressure and released easily and gracefully. They must never be struck or played with a hard touch.

Special accompaniment exercises for Left Hand.

TRIADS (Three tone chords)

These are played according to first instructions for double notes; hold the hand and fingers *in shape,* and firm. Do not practise these until previous exercises are mastered.

ARPEGGIOS (The tones of the chord played in separate succession.)

Write the fingering

The fingers must lift high and strike with quickness and precision. Do not push the keys, or use the hand or arm to assist the fingers. Be sure that each finger lifts quickly to "up position" the instant the next finger *strikes at* its key.

BEGINNING ON A COUNT OTHER THAN "ONE."

Thus far, each example begins on the first count in the measure. This is t   Aablish a strong feeling for the fundamental rhythms in their simplest forms. Music is also so written as to commence on other than the first count of the measure, in which case it begins with an incomplete measure consisting of one or several notes. The last measure in the piece, or the measure before the double bar, is also an incomplete measure containing the remaining note values omitted from the first measure. This shortening of the last measure is not a sure guide to the counting of the first measure, for many composers do not observe this custom.

four   one, two, three

three, four   one, two

two, three, four   one

Study and explain these further examples

How may you know the first group is not a Triplet?

Observe the effect of the change of accent

EAR-TRAINING: THE SCOTCH SCALE, INTERVALS, RHYTHM.

The Campbells are Coming
Famous Old Scotch Song for Bagpipes and Drums

The teacher should play this through slowly several times, then rapidly. Continue until the pupil becomes so familiar with the piece that it can be sung from memory.

D.S. means "to the sign 𝄋"

When the pupil has caught the march swing of the rhythm, let him play the drum part as a strong rhythmic bass, well accented, the left hand playing Contra F-sharp, the right hand playing the open Fifth, on F♯ and C♯. Play each hand separately; then both hands together. Also let the pupil supply the accompaniment for two drums, rapping the rhythms on a table top; then on the piano.

ACCOMPANIMENT FOR TWO DRUMS

TWELVE EASY PIECES WITHOUT KEY SIGNATURES
In the easier major and minor Keys

For establishing a sense of hearing and recognizing different tonalities or Keys and to fix the fundamental five-finger positions firmly in the mind and the fingers. Transpose each piece to other Keys.

WOHLFAHRT

63

6-944-6

EXERCISES IN HAND CONTRACTION

Play at first with the repeats. Then straight through without the repeats

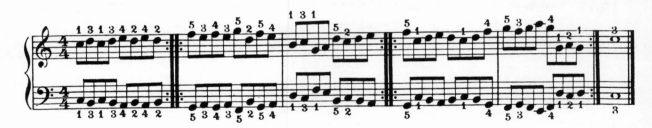

WOODEN SHOE DANCE

For the application of simple contraction

Arranged from an old tune by
CHARLES DENNEÉ

This piece requires slight changes from the fixed five-finger position of the hand. In the first measure of the right hand part the third finger plays the last note, although the second finger would naturally fall on the key. In the next measure the fourth finger plays the last note, which ordinarily would call for the fifth finger. There are similar changes to be observed in the left hand part. The hand retains its usual position, although the ends of the fingers, still curved, are brought closer together for the moment.

Make the accents decisive

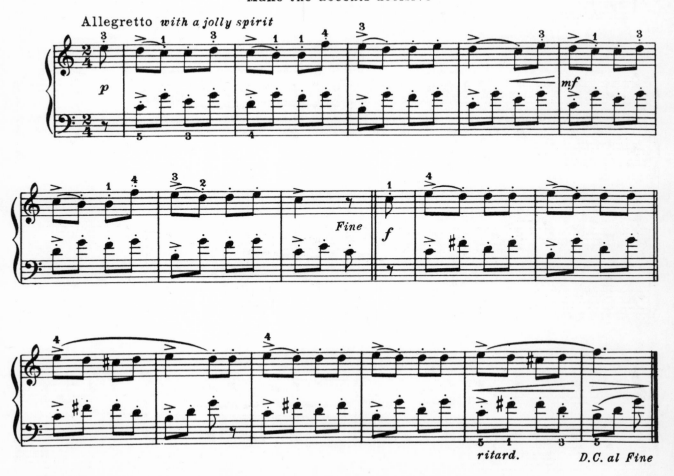

GRADE I-B
EXERCISES ON THE SCOTCH SCALE
To accustom the fingers to play on the black Keys

These little recreations are in the Key of F-sharp Major, which has a Key-signature of six sharps. It is essential that the pupil learn the exact location of the Keys upon which the sharps are played. A sharped note is played one halfstep higher than the note would be played if not sharped. C#, D#, F#, G#, and A#. are played upon the black key to the right of each respective white key, E# must be played upon the next higher white key, since there is no black key to the right of E.

RECOLLECTIONS OF INFANT DAYS

Retain the normal hand position, as on the white keys; keep the fingers curved.

A SONG

Copy these recreations without the Key-signature, and while the Keyboard is out of sight place the sharps in their proper positions.

The same effect can be produced with six flats in the Key-signatures. The black notes would then be Gb, Ab, Bb, Db, and Eb, with Cb played on the next white key below C. Copy the preceding pieces in G-flat, *using accidentals.*

FIRST BLACK KEY POSITION

Practice finger exercises built upon the five black key positions.

SECOND BLACK KEY POSITION

THE SCOTCH SCALE

FINGER SUBSTITUTION

For the holding down or repetition of a key, it is often necessary to substitute a finger other than the one by which it had previously been depressed. The object is to free the fingers for other notes, and avoid an unnecessary passing of the thumb under the hand or of the hand over the thumb. This changing or substitution of fingers on the same key is applied in several ways.

Legato Substitution — pure undetached finger impulses

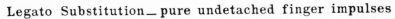

Substitution following a released key

Substitution following a slur ending

Substitution in rapid passages

Substitution on Double Notes following slur endings, and requiring a staccato pressure touch.

SILENT SUBSTITUTION. Preparation for legatissimo and extensions
Ths substitution is made on the second half of the note value

CONSECUTIVE FINGER SUBSTITUTION for rapid repetitions of the same key

With broken triad accompaniment

Lightly Tripping Along

H. BERENS, Op. 70

At The Circus

Also transpose to F major

HAND CONTRACTION

Exercises for moving the hand along the keyboard, applying same fingering on different groups of notes.

Keep the hand quiet. Do not move the wrist or arm in the slightest degree as regards pumping, or up and down motions. Practise each hand alone until absolute sureness is attained.

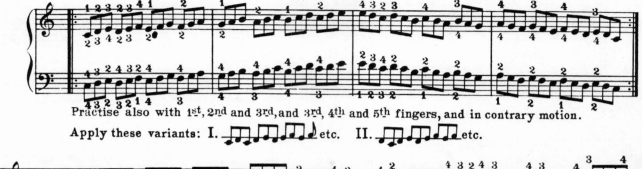

Practise also with 1st, 2nd and 3rd, and 3rd, 4th and 5th fingers, and in contrary motion.

Apply these variants: I. ♩♩♩ etc. II. ♩♩♩ etc.

Practise both fingerings

Also apply the dotted group rhythms; transpose to the keys of G, D, A, E and F, learning each thoroughly before proceeding to the next.

FIRST VELOCITY STUDY

CORNELIUS GURLITT
Op. 83, № 1

70

EXERCISES IN DOUBLE NOTES
With Touch Variety

Hold the hand in position, keeping the fingers curved and firm. Play with a pressure at first, later with a slight motion of the arm (up for the rests, down for the notes.)

When under complete control in these two ways practise with wrist action, lifting the hand from the wrist for the rest, bringing it down (moving from the wrist) for the notes; always hold the hand and fingers in the same shape when moving on the wrist; do not stiffen or strain the muscles, keep them always free and flexible. Never throw the hand up, or down against the keys, and never assist with the arm; keep it quiet and poised (supported).

Thoroughly learn each repeated section, in above exercises, before proceeding to the next. Also play all these examples with the rests omitted.

35-735-60

THE FIFE AND DRUM CORPS PASSING BY

A group of four sixteenth notes equals two eighth notes.

THEODOR OESTEN

Fife *The right hand one octave higher than written*

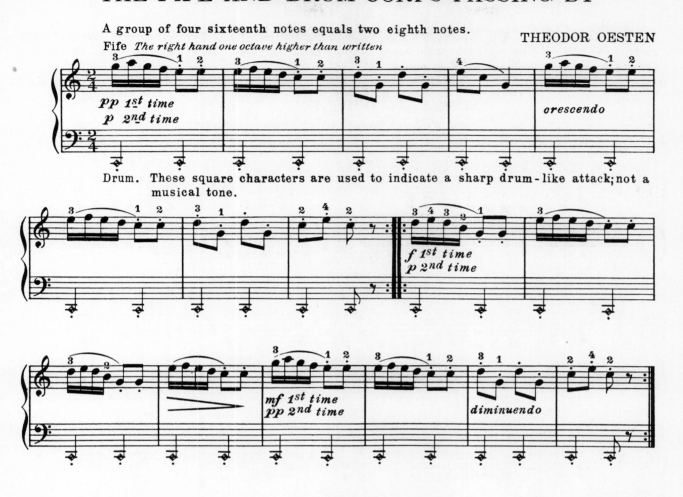

Drum. These square characters are used to indicate a sharp drum-like attack; not a musical tone.

IN A CANOE

MORE ADVANCED DOUBLE NOTES

By the use of double notes we are enabled to add other parts, or voices, to make the harmony more complete. Double notes in both hands produce full harmony. These form the basis for the rich effects found in the larger musical forms.

SIMPLE ACCOMPANIMENT MODELS
Which will fit many well-known songs.

STUDY
For finger quality

Notice the use of Treble Clef for reading practice in L.H., also change to Bass Clef to indicate the same keys.

Allegretto

STUDY

By placing dots after each ♩ and ♪ the rhythm could be changed to $\frac{12}{8}$ (compound) rhythm.

The first note of each triplet is held through the group.

34-735-60

HAND EXPANSION
SLOW DANCE
Introducing use of the pedal

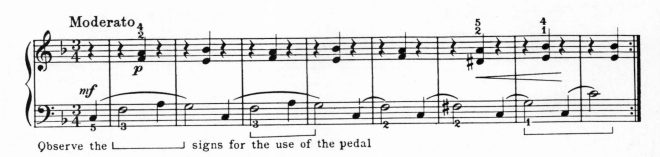

Observe the ⌐___⌐ signs for the use of the pedal

STUDY IN EXPANSION

A. LOESCHHORN

PLAYING MOVING FIGURES WHILE HOLDING ANOTHER TONE

The classical composers were exponents of the polyphonic, or contrapuntal school. Counterpoint means point against point___ two or more voices moving in opposition to one another. These exercises are a preparation for polyphonic playing.

COMBINATION OF HELD TONES AND STACCATO
For Independence and Control

[−] Tenuto mark; press the tone, and cling to the key for the full value of the note.

The effect desired is as though a half note were written on top of the first eighth note, as at A, in the example. This form of writing is often used because of its simplicity. Strictly speaking B, C or D would be more correct, although D is seldom used.

Polyphonic playing does not alway require the continued holding of one key while playing others. Bach, in the Preludes and Fugues of his Well-Tempered Clavichord, probably employed this more often than the other composers of the old classical school.

Many of the studies and pieces in these early pages are written in an elementary form of two-voice counterpoint, or polyphony. This is more noticeable in those pieces in which the voices move in opposite directions, or where a figure or passage moves in opposition to a more or less stationary or slow moving melody.

THEME AND VARIATIONS

A. EHMANT

legatissimo, sustain the first note in each measure

FIRST VARIATION

SECOND VARIATION

SECOND VELOCITY STUDY

CORNELIUS GURLITT
Op. 83, No. 2

KEYBOARD SHIFTING OF THE HAND

Thus far the hands have been confined to a fixed position over certain keys. With the exception of slight expansions from the fundamental five - finger position, there has been no change in the location of the hand.

It now becomes necessary to shift the hands from this fixed position over one group of keys to other keyboard positions more or less distant.

In many cases these changes of position can be accomplished by means of an expansion and contraction, but it is also accomplished by crossing a finger over the thumb, putting the thumb under the hand or by substituting fingers on the same key.

If the new key position is too far removed to permit this, the hand is carried along horizontally by the forearm and placed over the next key position. This must be done easily, quietly and gracefully.

SHIFTING KEYBOARD POSITION
By expansion and finger substitution

TWO LITTLE PIECES
For the Study of Phrasing and Staccato

A Rose Garden

L. KÖHLER

Moderato con grazia *(moderately and with grace)*

Release last note of slur according to rules for *releasing* staccato notes

Dance of the Clowns

C. DENNÉE

Allegro giocoso

Agile Fingers

Notice and study the sharps and naturals before beginning to practise.

C. FREDRIC

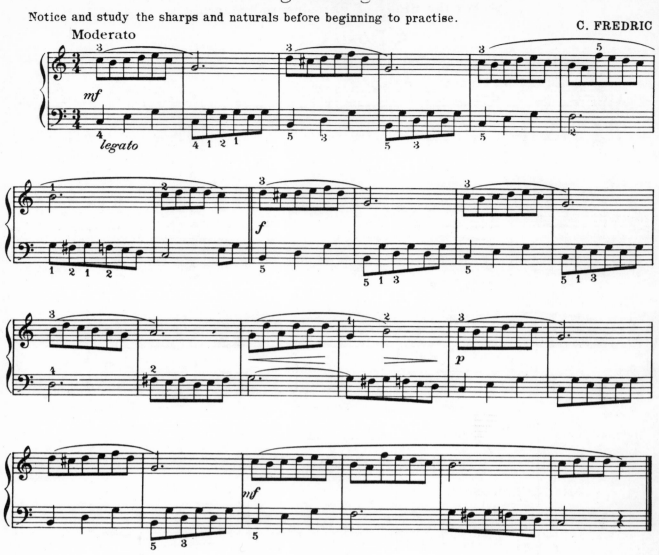

EXERCISES FOR CROSSING FINGER OVER AND PASSING THUMB UNDER

Retain the curved position of fingers. Do not turn the wrist, or push up with the knuckles.

Do not practise the following until the previous exercises are thoroughly mastered.

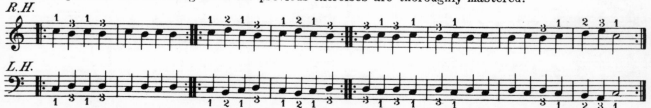

Practice daily until thoroughly mastered. Also beginning on G, D, A and E, with the necessary 27-735-60 accidentals to retain the same diatonic intervals.

A Little Dialogue

HEINRICH WOHLFAHRT

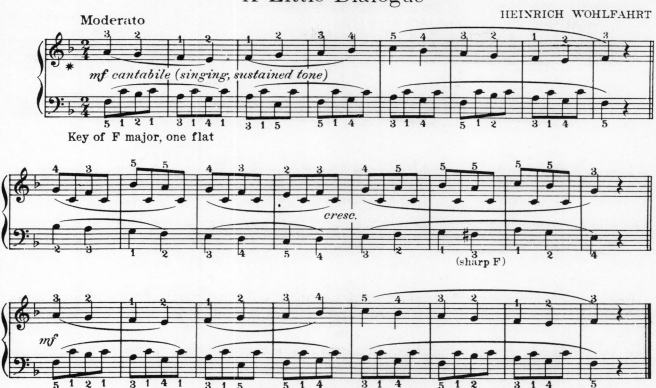

Key of F major, one flat

✻ The ♭ sign is placed on the line for B at the beginning of each brace to indicate that every B in the piece must be flatted. This is called the "key signature," and saves printing flats throughout the piece.

EXERCISES FOR REPEATING NOTES WITH SAME FINGER
also for practise in holding one key while playing others

Practice very slowly, without forcing the tone, keeping the fingers close to the keys. The fingers must not lift high, or strike; they must move easily on the knuckles and gently take hold of each repeated key. The hand must be held quiet but without stiffness or straining.

Do not push or bear weight on held keys; the finger must simply rest easily on the keys to steady the hand.

82

Peasant's Polka

Allegro vivace *(fast with vivacity)* *(ligero con vivacidad)*

SCHÖNE MINKA

Russian Folk Song

Moderato

58-735-60

STUDY IN LITTLE RUNS

PREPARATORY EXERCISE Refer to previous exercises for passing thumb under and fingers over.

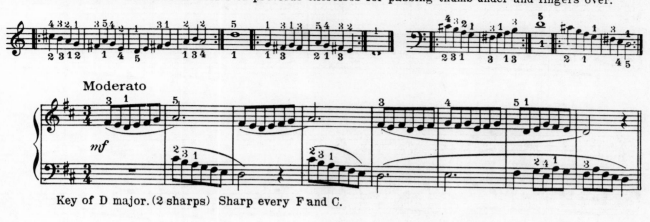

Moderato

Key of D major. (2 sharps) Sharp every F and C.

A Simple Story

Notice the use of the Treble Clef for reading practice in left hand.

J. ASCHER

* Andante (*rather slowly*)

p semplice (in a simple manner)

Observe the accidentals ♯ and ♭.

Fine.

* The literal meaning of Andante is "going," or moving.

32-735-60

Early Morn

F. BEYER

Allegretto

mf dolce

legato

Key of **F** major. Flat **B** every time it appears in the piece.

By placing **dots** after each half and quarter **note** this piece would be in $\frac{12}{8}$ (compound) rhythm.

The Cuckoo

Staccato Study

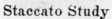

KÖHLER

(In what key is this piece written?)

A CONVERSATION

CORNELIUS GURLITT
Op. 82, № 44

Round Dance

Application of slurs and staccato

C. FREDRIC

Allegretto

Write the proper fingering. Watch the sharps and study them.

Fine

D.C. al Fine

EXERCISE IN DOUBLE AND SINGLE NOTES

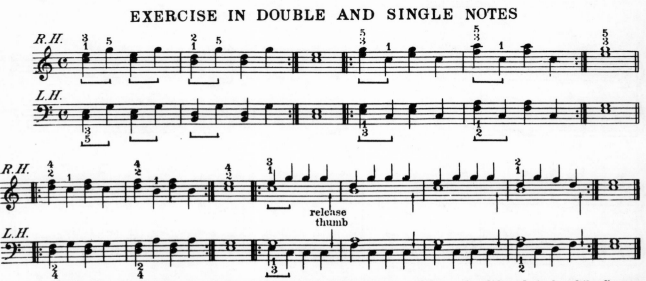

Be sure that the double notes are played exactly together with careful, precise lift and stroke of the fingers. When mastered in legato, practise in staccato. Groups within brackets form triads.

29-735-60

STUDY IN DOUBLE NOTES
and changing fingers on same key

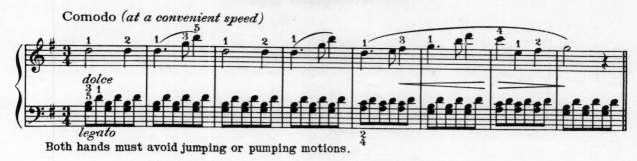

Both hands must avoid jumping or pumping motions.

This study is in G major (one sharp.) The sharp sign at beginning each brace indicates that every F in the study is to be sharped. (See introductory remarks on sharps, flats etc.)

Morning Song

Do not jump the hand on repeated notes with same finger

C. FREDRIC

Moderato

FUNDAMENTAL BROKEN TRIADS
In the easier Keys

Repeat each 20 times. Keep the fingers well curved; strive for perfect finger-action. Memorize the flats and sharps in the different Key signatures. These are to be played with separate hands, slowly at first, with accurate motions of the fingers. Learn, and memorize each separate Key before going on to the next one.

REPEATED THIRDS
Using Pressure Touch

Repeat each measure many times.

A *legato effect* is produced by not permitting the keys to rise to their original position.

SLOW MOVING THIRDS
Double Trill Preparation

PROGRESSIVE THIRDS

32-744-52

THE SPINNING WHEEL

First employment of sixteenth note groups

Allegro *(Slowly moderately fast-fast)*

How many sixteenths notes to a count; to a half count?

PARADE OF THE BOY SCOUTS

PASCONET

Tempo di Marcia In March Tune

sempre staccato (always staccato)

The word "simile" could be used instead of "sempre staccato"

33-744-52

THEME AND VARIATIONS

TH. KULLAK

Variation III

Variation IV

Variation V

FAMILIAR SCHOOL DAY SONGS AND HYMN TUNES
Introducing the Key Signatures F, G, A and D major
A CHILDHOOD HYMN

The fingering in these pieces affords special practice in expansion, contraction, and substitution, without thumb passing or finger crossing.

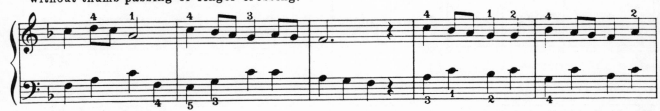

AMERICA

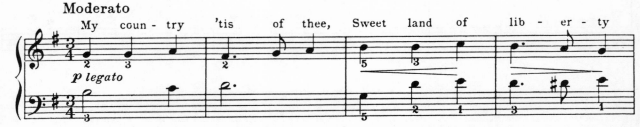

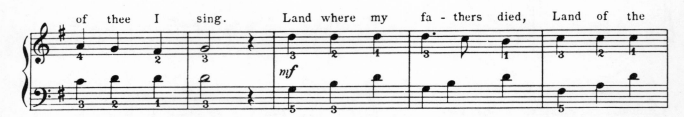

BABY'S LULLABY
The Song My Mother Sang

AN OLD SOUTHERN SONG

Play with a sweetly singing tone

FROM AN OLD HYMN BOOK

GEO. F. ROOT

THE BOYS SING AN OLD FAVORITE

Johnnie sings the solo, and plays an accompaniment with one finger

Write the meaning of all the signs used.

THE SCOTCH FIFE AND DRUM CORPS PLAYS A DANCE TUNE

Allegro con spirito *(With spirit)*

C. DENNÉE

TWO DESCRIPTIVE PIECES
Introducing transient changes or modulations into different Keys

DOWN IN THE MEADOW THE GRASS IS SO GREEN

A. LOESCHHORN

Allegro ma non troppo

What Keys do F♯ and F♮ make; B♭ and B?

Key of A minor. Why?

KITTENS PLAYING
A little Scherzo

For finger substitution; also for phrasing — which results from the observance of the slurs. The piece is in C major; are there any Key changes, or modulations?

A. LOESCHHORN

Allegro moderato

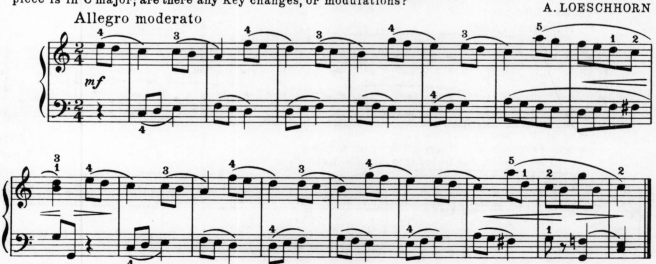

The Juggler
For Skill in Changing Keyboard Position

Continue practising until speed is acquired.

Allegro moderato

Observe slurs; remember what effect the staccato note has at end of slur and give the note the exact value indicated in first part of book.

Study
For independence between the hands

Practise for speed
Allegro *(fast)*

Key of A minor

cresc. (crescendo) Increasing in strength
dim. (diminuendo) Decreasing in strength

Fine

Key of C major

D. C. al Fine

EXERCISES IN MOVING LEGATO DOUBLE NOTES (THIRDS)

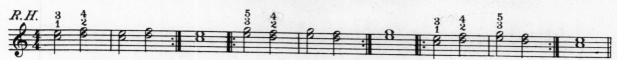

Play the notes exactly together; practise also in quarter and eighth notes.

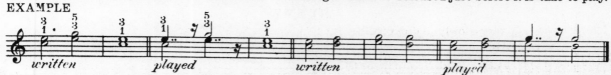

Transpose to G, D, A, E and F major.

If one of the notes is repeated in the next Third the finger must be released just before it is time to play.
EXAMPLE

written *played* *written* *played*

Practise continually until this point is thoroughly mastered; it is the basis of all legato playing in double notes.
Transpose also to G, D, A, E and F major.

STUDIES

The pupil must be careful to strike the two notes of the thirds precisely together and play strictly legato.

98

Moderato

Moderato

STUDY

Practise very slowly and carefully

Moderato

Avoid straining or hand motion.

Continue practising this study until control and skill are attained

50-735-60

BROKEN THIRDS IN EIGHTH NOTES

These have been delayed until the pupil has acquired considerable control and equality in the fingers. In cases of talent above the average these may, at the discretion of the teacher, be taken up earlier.

Name the "Keys" in which these exercises are written. Prove it!

Each repeat 30 times

L.H. two octaves lower

PROGRESSIVE BROKEN THIRDS

Learn thoroughly in ascending, and in descending; then play in both directions without stopping.

TRAVELING THROUGH THE KEYS
Name the modulations and give reasons

C. FREDRIC

Moderato

Exercises In Repeated Triads and Inversions

in the easier major "Keys"

Practise slowly at first.

Repeat each measure many times.

When learned in quarter notes, play in *eighth notes*, two notes to a count at the same metronome speed as when played in quarter notes. Continue to play these daily. Learn each Key thoroughly before proceeding to the next. Slow but sure progress is the key to ultimate success as a pianist.

THE HAND-ORGAN

Introducing consecutive finger substitution

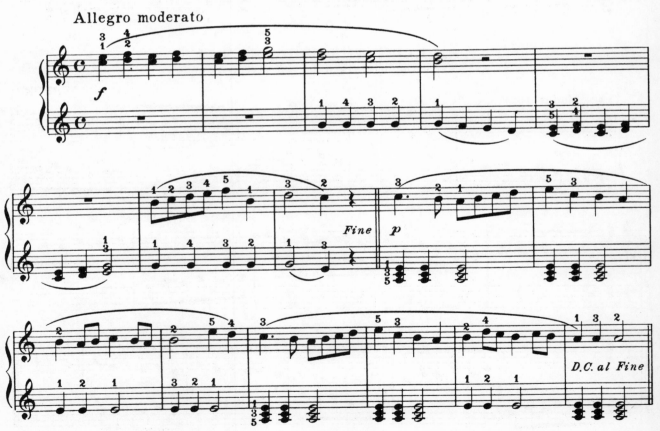

THIRD VELOCITY STUDY

C. GURLITT
Op. 83, Nº 3

FOURTH VELOCITY STUDY

C. GURLITT
Op. 83, No 4.

MIXED TRIADS IN CLOSE FIXED POSITION
Introducing triads other than simple fundamental forms.

These are played according to the instructions for double notes; hold the hand and fingers firmly in shape. Do not practise until previous exercises are mastered.

At first, repeat each measure many times; then play as written. Eventually play straight through omitting all repeats.

WIDE EXPANSION — BROKEN CHORDS

A full chord is obtained by adding to a triad, the interval of an octave. Thus, the chord of C major will contain four tones -- a Root (C), a Third (E), a Fifth (G), and an Octave (C). A broken chord, the first form of the arpeggio, results when the tones of a full chord are played in regular succession, one after the other. Play very slowly at first; write the fingering.

Do not attempt to play solid full chords until they appear in the Second Grade.

FIRST FORM OF THE ARPEGGIO

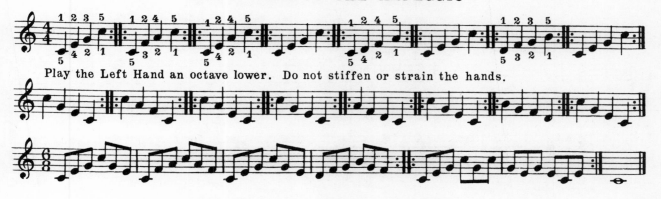

Play the Left Hand an octave lower. Do not stiffen or strain the hands.

SECOND FORM OF THE ARPEGGIO

The fingers must lift high and strike with quickness and precision. Do not push the keys, or use the hand or arm to assist the fingers. Be sure that each finger lifts quickly the instant the next finger strikes at its key.

LEFT HAND ACCOMPANIMENT FIGURES

ROLLED OR ARPEGGIATED TRIADS

A special sign is required to distinguish between an arpeggiated triad and a broken triad. This sign indicates that the triad should be rolled or quickly broken from the lowest to the highest note. It is like the effect produced when chords are played upon a harp; hence the term arpeggiated or "harp-like" chords. In slow music, the triad is rolled a trifle slower.

TWO SHORT STUDIES IN ROLLED CHORDS

CHARLES DENNÉE

KEYBOARD SHIFTING — ROLLED TRIADS

Song of the Hussars

For Practice in changing fingers on same key in Staccato playing

Marziale

EXERCISES IN INTERVAL PLAYING

Broken Thirds and Fourths

Transpose to G, D, A, E and F major.

MOVING BROKEN SIXTHS

Right Hand

Left Hand

Transpose to G, D, A, E and F major.

41-735-60 Pupils with large hands may also practise this fingering:

R. H.	1 4 2 5	1 4 2 5
L. H.	5 2 4 1	5 2 4 1

STUDY
For the application of Interval playing

Allegro

legato

STUDY

Allegro

legato

Mazurka

Allegro moderato

C. CZERNY

Find and analyze all triad and broken triad applications

Waltz

Allegro vivace

C. CZERNY

THIRDS IN EIGHTH NOTES
In the easier major Keys

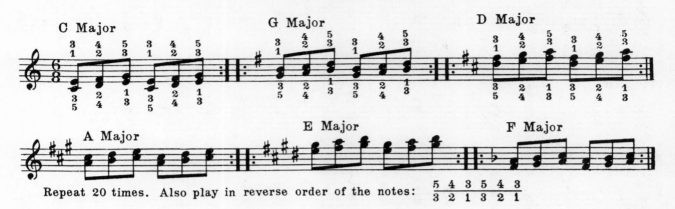

Repeat 20 times. Also play in reverse order of the notes: $\frac{5\ 4\ 3\ 5\ 4\ 3}{3\ 2\ 1\ 3\ 2\ 1}$

MOVING BROKEN THIRDS

Also play the reverse order of the notes. Practise with each hand alone. Do not play the hands together until the early part of Grade 2.

The playing of double notes is a technical problem which can be mastered only through patient and persistent practice. Ability to play the notes together, and to attain speed and fluency in moving pairs of fingers, is a goal which every serious-minded pupil should endeavor to reach.

STUDY IN BROKEN THIRDS

For developing an easy wrist action

THIRDS

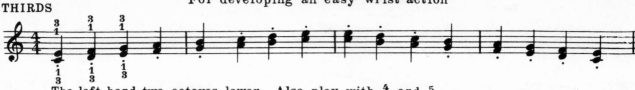

The left hand two octaves lower. Also play with $\frac{4}{2}$ and $\frac{5}{3}$

FOURTHS

Also play with $\frac{5}{2}$

SIXTHS

Also play with $\frac{4}{1}$

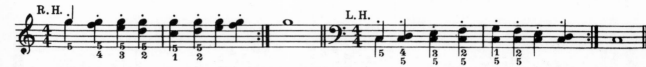

Name all of the intervals. Also practise with a portamento touch.

STACCATO BROKEN DOUBLE NOTES

THIRDS

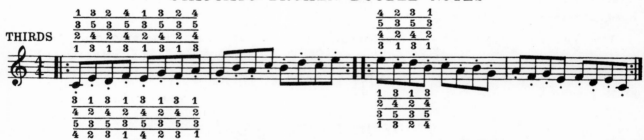

Practise broken Fourths, and broken Sixths, using the fingering as in the staccato Fourths and Sixths. These broken note exercises should also be played very legato, with precise finger action. Use all the fingerings. The intervals of a Fourth do not sound well when played consecutively up the scale, but they afford excellent practice for the weaker fingers.

STACCATO BROKEN TRIADS
First and Second Inversions

These combine intervals of a Third and a Fourth.
Apply the following exercises to triads built on G, D, A, E, F.

FIRST INVERSION

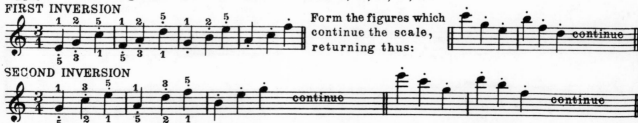

Form the figures which continue the scale, returning thus:

SECOND INVERSION

Also practise these inversions legato, and transpose to the Keys of G, D, A, E and F.

Country Dance

A Study for easy shifting of hand to different keyboard positions
and practise in simple double notes with wrist action.

The last note under each slur should be shortened in value.

Allegro moderato

KÖHLER

Key of G; one sharp
Staccato (dots over notes)

S 107

Allegretto   STUDY IN STACCATO SIXTHS

36-735-60

And He Said

TH. GRAY

SONG

(From Anna Magdalene's Notebook)

J.S. BACH

BROKEN TRIADS
Moving through the the positions in succession

Pupils with large hands may also practise this fingering: $\frac{\text{R.H. } 123 \quad 124 \quad 124 \quad 123}{\text{L.H. } 321 \quad 421 \quad 421 \quad 321}$. This prepares the hand for the broken chords of four notes, C E G C, G C E G, in which the 1st, 2nd and 5th fingers are always used, with a choice between the 3rd or 4th finger according to the interval. Fundamentally, if the interval is a Fourth play with the 3rd and 5th fingers; if it is a Third play with 4th and 5th fingers.

When well under control extend these exercises to a compass of two, three and four octaves.

STUDY IN MOTION

DENNÉE

How should the Pedal be applied to this Study?

APPLICATION OF BROKEN TRIADS
With Keyboard shifting in legato and staccato figures
In the Key of F major

THE HARP PLAYER

STUDY
Staccato Broken Triad figures

WOHLFAHRT

THE MILL

SONG

116

SIMPLE SCALES

Review the first exercises for "crossing the fingers over and passing the thumb under." Then play the scale in C Major, as given: also in G, D, A, E, and F Major.

SCALE OF C MAJOR

Observe that the fingering is the same in both hands when starting with the thumb and playing the fingers in their regular order (1, 2, 3, 1, 2, 3, 4.) All scales that start on white keys are fingered the same as C major with the exception of F major, in the right hand, and B Major, in the left hand, where the regular fingering would bring the thumb on a black key. In scale playing, the thumb always falls on a white key.

MANNER OF FINGERING THESE EXCEPTIONS

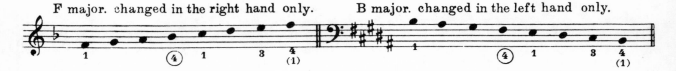

Adapt the scale pattern to other Keys as follows:

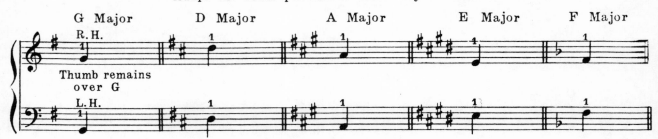

Additional scale patterns to be applied to scales in all these keys.

A diatonic scale is made up of whole-steps and half-steps; where are the half-steps? Name the correct degrees in each scale starting on a white key. Then write them, using sharps or flats before the proper notes, in place of the Key signatures.

46-744-52

NAMES OF THE SCALE DEGREES

To identify the chords built upon the different scale degrees, each scale degree has its own distinctive name.

These names should be applied to the scale degrees in the various scale passages and exercises.

1. First scale degree is called the TONIC.
2. Second scale degree is called the SUPER-TONIC.
3. Third scale degree is called the MEDIANT.
4. Fourth scale degree is called the SUB-DOMINANT.
5. Fifth scale degree is called the DOMINANT.
6. Sixth scale degree is called the SUB-MEDIANT.
7. Seventh scale degree is called the LEADING TONE.

Of these the Tonic, Dominant, and Sub-dominant are the Roots of the strong chords—the more important chords in each Key. Simple pieces and studies are mainly built upon these chords.

THE IMPORTANCE OF SCALE PLAYING

Up to this point, the pupil has been drilled upon all the fundamental technical material that is used in pianoforte playing, with the exception of scales, scales in octaves, chords, and certain principles which can be studied only after further advancement in playing has been attained.

The world's great pianists attained their pre-eminence by assiduous labor on technical exercises, especially scales. So much do they appreciate this fact that they practise for years upon scales, exercises made up from scales, scale fragments, and combinations of these with broken chords and other purely technical figures. Examine the classics and observe how music is constructed. Never give up the slow practice of scale passages. Equality, skill, endurance, and all that is essential in a well equipped technique, are possible only through ceaseless, careful work upon scales.

SCALE VARIANTS AND FRAGMENTS

Scale passages are frequently written with one or more of the consecutive degrees omitted. For example, a passage may begin on C and progress upward omitting D; or it may begin on C and progress downward omitting A. Various applications of irregular scale passages will be found in almost all studies and pieces. In whatever music you are playing, search for such variants or fragments of scale passages, and practise each as a special technical exercise, thereby increasing finger independence and fluency in the playing of other than straight scale passages.

The scale may also be played in Triplets, using variants on two general models. The first—up one octave and return, three times. This brings the accents on different tones in each repetition, with a strong ending on the key note at the end of the third descending scale. The second—a combined ten-note scale, ascending and descending, once.

Contrast the scale in Triplets with the scale in Doublets, or groups of two notes, up and down through one octave; also in Quadruplets, or groups of four notes, up and down one octave twice. Later it can be played in Doublets through two octaves and return; in Triplets through three octaves; and in Quadruplets through four octaves.

S18P–I–138(1c)

The Practice of the Scale

EXERCISES

For passing the thumb under

Practise these on the corresponding scale degrees, in other Keys.

THE EASIER MAJOR SCALES
Beginning on White Keys.

When the scale is learned so that it can be played easily and fluently, practise it in the following manner.

Also the reverse, starting with the 5th finger in each hand

‖: 5 4 3 2 1 3 2 1 :‖: 2 1 2 3 1 2 3 4 :‖

SCALES WITH THE HANDS TOGETHER

When the scales are well learned with separate hands, they should be played with the hands together. Do not play the scales in parallel motion until they are first thoroughly mastered in contrary motion. In scales in contrary motion the same fingers play at the same time in both hands, which makes it much easier to learn and to establish correct habits of fingering. Continue the practise of the preparatory exercises for scale playing even after the scales seem to have become easy to play. Technique is a means to an end. Technical development should always be in advance of the requirements of the pieces.

Write the scales in all Keys, using this model.

47-744-52

After writing the following scales, supply the correct Key signatures and the proper fingering. Exercise care in making the notes. Write and practise one scale at a time, applying all the forms previously given.

G MAJOR
R. H.
L. H.

D MAJOR
R. H.
L. H.

A MAJOR
R. H.
L. H.

E MAJOR
R. H.
L. H.

F MAJOR (Remember the difference in the fingering)
R. H.
L. H.

48-744-52

SKATING

C. FREDRIC

Allegretto

LEARNING TO RUN

H. WOHLFAHRT

Allegro moderato

122

Study
For Independence and Speed

Continue practising for speed

Allegretto

Children's Ball

Allegretto moderato

46-755-60

SUCCESSION OF ALL THE KEYS AND THEIR RELATIONSHIP
Fundamental Tonic Triads in Progressive Order

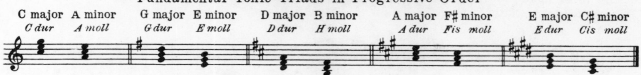

These are the Tonic (key note) Chords, built on the degree of the Scale

Scales having some key signature belong to the same tonal family, so to speak, and are therefore related. A minor is the relative minor of C major, but it is _not_ the Scale of C minor. C major is the relative major of A minor, etc. Gradually learn these relations, but do not start too soon. Learn the "key note" scales first beyond a possibility of a doubt.

SCALE STUDY

Change these studies to G major, name and think the notes in that key before practising. Also to D major. This is called transposition.

The Brook

Notice change of clef for same position

D.C. al Fine

56-735-60

FIFTH VELOCITY STUDY

C. GURLITT
Op. 83, No 5.

SIXTH VELOCITY STUDY

C. GURLITT
Op. 83, № 6.

There are two kinds of grace notes, the short grace note, or acciaccatura, and the long grace note, or appoggiatura; also called "crushed tone", and "leaning note."

The grace note is indicated by a very small note.

Short grace notes have an oblique dash through the tail of the note stem, whereas long grace notes are written without this dash.

Long grace notes are generally given their full face value, and receive the accent.

Short grace notes are quickly crushed into the following note.

EXAMPLES

Short grace note. (crushed tone)

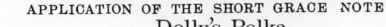

Long grace note. (leaning note)

Figure out these values and apply them hereafter when grace notes occur.

APPLICATION OF THE SHORT GRACE NOTE
Dolly's Polka

Allegro grazioso (*fast and gracefully*)   C. DENNÉE

Key of D major (2 sharps)

Dutch Dance

Allegro giocoso

Clown and Pantaloon
WALTZ

F. BEYER

Play this ending 1st time   Play this ending on repeat

1 omit on repeat

2

✱) Observe the **difference in notation** of 1st measure (L.H.) Both have the same effect when played.

Minuet from Don Juan
Introducing stretches in double note playing.

W. A. MOZART

SCALES AND STACCATO

mark all of the Key changes

SHEPHERD'S PIPE
(From Sonatina, Op. 36, № 3)

CLEMENTI

STUDY

TWO EASY SCALE STUDIES

L. KOHLER, Op. 151, No. 9

Allegro commodo

SIGNS AND ABBREVIATIONS

These are endings (1st ending, 2nd ending) to save space and pages in music. The first time through play 1st ending, then repeat and play through to 1st ending again but this time skip 1st ending and play 2nd ending.

When a piece is marked *D. C.* it is a general rule to play through the 1st part, (on the Da Capo, or repeat) to the word Fine, without observing the repeat marks. But they should be observed the first time the composition or movement is played through, especially if they consist of short passages with two endings.

D.C. al ⊕ *e poi la Coda* Go back to the beginning, play to the sign, ⊕, and then go immediately to the Coda. *Coda* An ending or finishing passage. *D.S.* 𝄋 means *Dal Segno*, go back to the sign 𝄋.

MUSICAL TERMS

The definitions given here are for the practical application of these terms

Andante— Generally accepted as meaning rather slowly. **Lento, slow. Adagio, quite slow.**

Andantino— Less Andante; generally accepted as meaning a little faster than Andante.

Moderato— At a moderate, comfortable speed; not fast. **Marziale, March-like.**

Allegro— Fast, lively. **Allegro assai, very fast. Allegro giocoso, joyfully.**

Allegretto— In a bright, cheerful style; not so fast as Allegro, faster than Moderato.

Comodò— At an accomodating or comfortable speed. **Tempo di Polka, in the time of a Polka.**

Piu Allegro— Faster than the preceding; piu, more, Allegro, fast. **Presto, very fast.**

dolce— Sweetly *scherzando*, dance like. *grazioso*, gracefully.

poco or un poco— means "a little" and is used before some other term to modify it.

poco a poco— Little by little; gradually. *crescendo*, growing louder; *diminuendo*, diminishing in volume.

con— with, ex, *con Ped.*, with the Pedal. *espressivo*, with expression, applied to a song-like melody.

meno. Less; ex, *meno allegro*, less fast— *meno forte*, less loud. *un poco adagio* rather slow.

mosso. movement, motion; ex, *piu mosso*, more motion (faster) *meno mosso*, less motion (slower).

accelerando, *stringendo*, growing faster; *ritard*, *ritenuto*, *rallentando*, growing slower.

vivo } with life; vivaceously. *con spirito*, with spirit.
vivace—

ma non troppo, but not to much. *maestoso*, majestically.

THE PEDALS

The right hand pedal is called the Damper Pedal (not the Loud Pedal.) It's function is to raise all the dampers away from the strings at once, thus allowing all the tones that are played while the pedal is pressed down, to be sustained Letting the pedal up drops the dampers against the strings again and stops the tone.

In playing without the pedal the putting down of the key raises the individual damper for the strings of that one tone only.

The left hand pedal is called the Soft Pedal and in upright pianos moves the hammers closer to the strings, thus shortening the stroke, making the key action lighter, and producing a soft tone with the same amount of finger force. In Grand pianos it shifts the key board to the right, and as in the earlier instruments it shifted far enough to allow the hammers to strike only one of three strings it was called Una Corda (one string,) which term is in general use to-day. The words "tre corde" indicate the release of the soft pedal.

The word "Ped." indicates the pressing down of the damper pedal; the sign ✳ indicates the release of it.

If simply the word "Ped." is used continually, without any star (✳) the pedal should be pressed down at the first word "Ped.", held until the next "Ped." and then quickly released and immediately pressed down again just as the note over the word is played.

The use of the pedals should be delayed until every other difficulty has been mastered. Do not begin its use earlier than the place indicated in this volume except for special practise and experiment.

In modern editions certain signs underneath the bass staff are used to indicate the pressing and release of the Damper pedals. Modern pedal indications: ⌞⌟ ⌞⌟ ⌞ ⌟ ⌟⌞ ⋀ ⋀
Equivalents in older notation: Ped. ✳ Ped. ✳ Ped.   ✳ Ped. Ped. Ped. ✳

SECOND GRADE SECTION
Technical Exercises

For developing equality in finger action and tone power combined with steadily increasing fluency and velocity.

FIVE-FINGER FIGURES IN VARIED GROUPINGS

These exercises should be practiced throughout the Second Grade, using only a few at a time. Attain the best possible results, both in independence and speed (in several different keys,) before proceeding with the practice of new ones.

Each exercise must be repeated at least 10 or 20 times, omitting the closing note until the last repetition. Practice at first each hand separately, afterward with both hands together, but always with a quiet hand. Begin very slowly and increase the tempo gradually, as the fingers gain strength and flexibility.

These exercises should be practiced in all keys, using the same fingering.

Pay strict attention to correct hand position and precise motions of the fingers.

ALOYS SCHMITT, Op. 16

FIGURES MOVING AROUND HELD KEYS
Transpose to other Keys, the simpler ones first

Also practise with the hands reversed, the right hand notes in the left hand, and vice-versa.

137

The Anchored Hand, with single fingers repeated

Great care must be exercised to avoid stiffness. Do not force the tone in the playing fingers, and do not push stiffly against the held keys.

CONSECUTIVE SUCCESSION OF DOUBLE THIRDS

Avoid tension in the hand or wrist. Play with moving fingers, exactly together, lifting an equal distance, and keeping the arm and hand quiet.

5-765-12

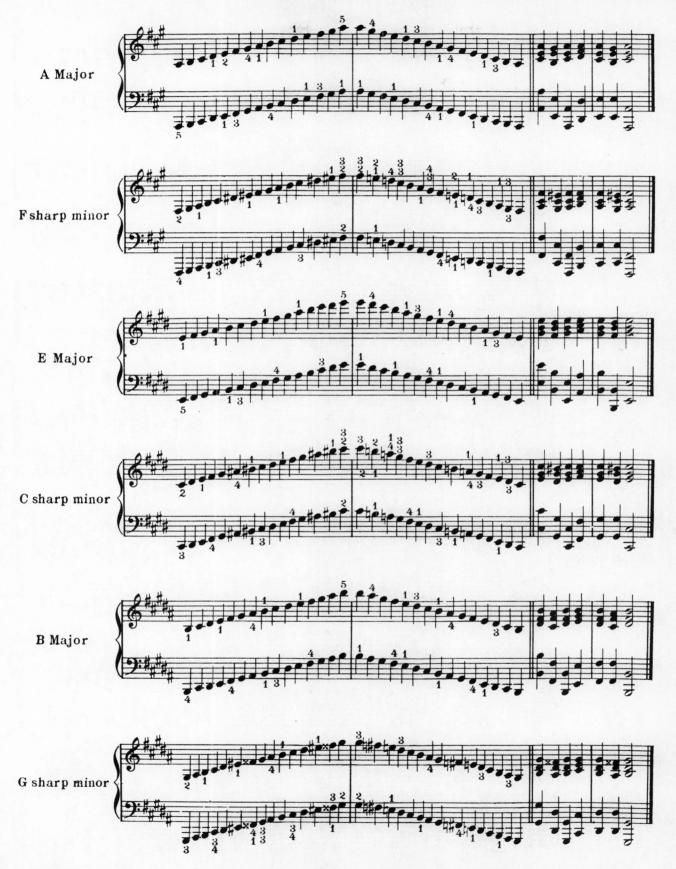

A Major

F sharp minor

E Major

C sharp minor

B Major

G sharp minor

31-734-33

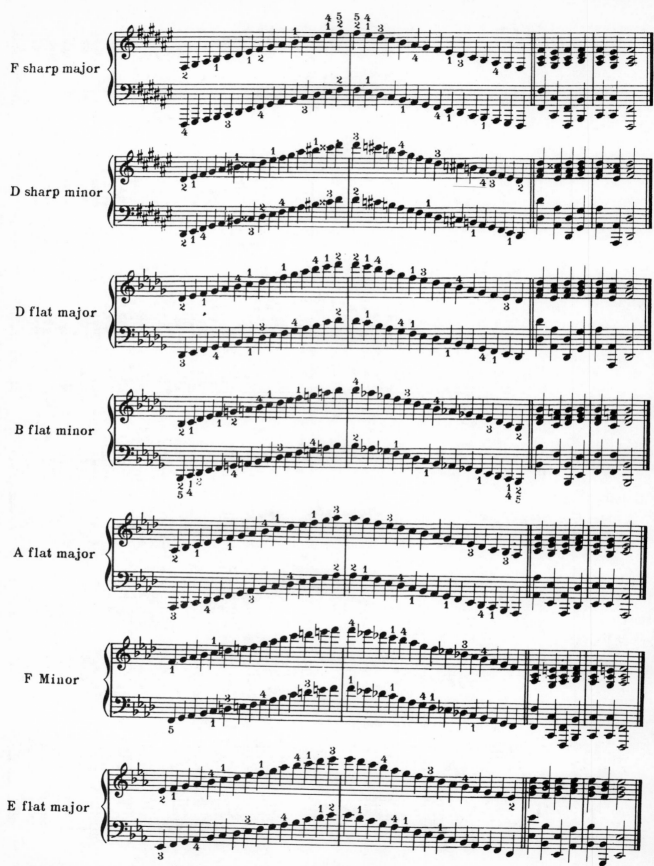

F sharp major

D sharp minor

D flat major

B flat minor

A flat major

F Minor

E flat major

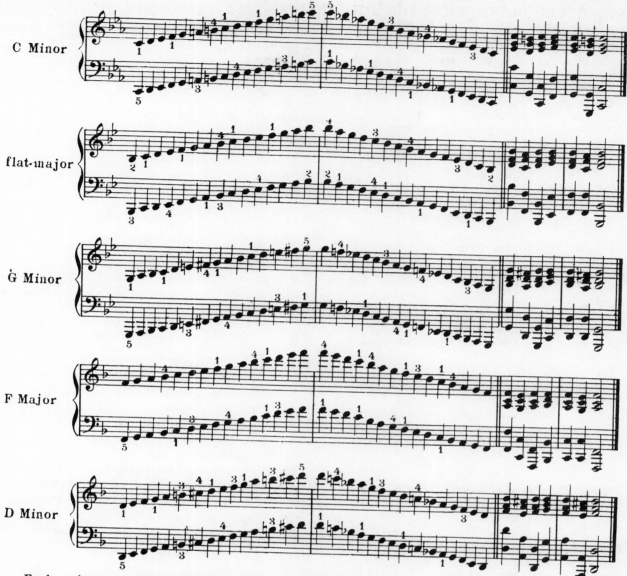

C Minor

flat-major

G Minor

F Major

D Minor

Each major scale is followed by its relative minor scale. This is done to establish the family relationship from the use of the same Key signature.

SCALES FOR FIRST HALF OF THE GRADE
C, G, D, A, E, B, and F major; A, E, G, and D minor.

SCALES FOR LAST HALF OF THE GRADE
Bb, Eb, Ab, Db, and Gb major; C, F and B minor; the previous scales to be reviewed for increased velocity and flexibility.

Play all scales with each hand alone until well learned. When the hands are first played together, play them in contrary motion, then in paralled motion. The Chromatic scale should be played a few times each day. Delay until the Third Grade those scales that are omitted in the above list.

N 33-734-33

PRACTICAL DEFINITIONS FOR THE MUSICAL TERMS USED IN THIS VOLUME.

A

Ad libitum *(ad lib.)* At the pleasure of the player
Adagio Very slowly
Allargando Larger; broaden
Anima - Animato Animated; with life
Assai Very; Much
A tempo In Time; the original speed again

B

Brillante In a brilliant manner

C

Calando Dying away; slower and softer
Cantabile In a singing style
Cantando Very singing tone quality
Con With
Con moto With motion or movement
Con brio With life, spirit
Con fuoco With fire, vigor
Con tenerezza Tenderly; with delicacy
Con fantasia See Ad libitum
Crescendo *(cresc)* Gradually louder and louder

D

Dim. e poco rit Gradually softer, and a slight ritard
Dolce Sweetly
Dolcissimo With extreme sweetness and delicacy
Dolce ed espressivo Sweetly and with expression
Decresc - Diminuendo Gradually growing softer

E

Espressivo - Con Espressione, With expression
Energico With energy

G

Giocoso In a jocular style; humorously
Grandioso Grandly; rather broad
Grave Extremely slow; solemnly
Grazioso - Con Grazia With grace; elegance
Graziosamente Extremely graceful

L

Largo Large; dignified
Leggierissimo As lightly as possible
Leggiero Lightly
Lento Slow

M

Maestoso Majestic in style
Maggiore Major
Marcato Marked, pronounced; bring out stronger
Marcato il canto The melody well emphasized
Metronome A clock instrument for ascertaining speed and beating exact time
Minore Minor
Molto Much
Molto cresc. Much crescendo
M.M.(♩=112) 112 quarters to a minute, one to each beat of metronome set at 112

1-857-10

N

Non Not
Non legato Not legato; the tones slightly detatched

P

Piu lento Slower than the preceding part
Poco A little
Poco piu tranquillo A little more tranquil; quieter
Prestissimo As fast as possible
Presto Very fast

R

Rallentando Gradually grow slower
Ritard *(rit)* ritardando, ritenuto, Hold back; grow slower
Rinforzando *(Rinf')* Reinforced; each tone strongly emphasized
Risoluto In a resolute determined manner
Rubato Flexible; Not in strict time; with expression

S

Scheroso - Scherzando In a light playful style
Semplice Simply
Sempre Always. **Sempre Staccato,** Continually staccato
Senza Without. **senza Ped.** Without Ped.
Simile Continue in the same way
Spiritoso - Con Spirito With spirit; bright; animated
Smorzando *(Smorz)* Suddenly smother the tone
Sostenuto Sustained; also means broader
Strepitoso Furiously
Stringendo *(String)* Considerable continual increase in speed

T

Tempo I - Tempo primo The same speed as at first
Temp di In the time, or speed of; **Tempo di Valse** In Waltz time
Tenuto *(Ten)* Clinging *(pressure)*; make tone sing
Triste Sad
Tristamente Very sadly

U

un A
un poco A little

V

Viva - Vivace Vivaceously; sprightly; with animation
Volante Flying; with extreme speed and deftness

The "classical" interpretation of those embellishments most commonly used are here applied to a piece. First play with all the embellishments omitted, to establish the melodic outline. Then add the embellishments, one at a time, studying and playing each individual illustration until it is memorized as to note values and manner of playing, and can be executed fluently. Refer to these illustrations when any embellishment is met in studies or pieces.

Names of the Various Embellishments

(a) Acciaccatura – crushed note; (b) Gruppetto – short slide; (c) The slide; (d) Acciaccatura, applied to double notes; (e) Prall-triller – inverted mordent; (f) Turn, over a note; (g) Inverted Turn, written as a slide, also its sign given; (h) Mordent; (i) Double Mordent; (k) Long Slide; (l) Trill with ending; (m) Turn, between two notes; (n) Turn between the notes of a dotted group; (o) Trill with acciaccatura, an indication to begin on the upper Trill note; (p) Appoggiatura, long grace note or leaning note.

TECHNICAL EXERCISES
For the last half of The Second Grade
TONIC CHORDS AND ARPEGGIOS
In the easier major and minor Keys

The models given for C Major are to be applied to the chords in the following Keys. Observe care in the playing of full chords, as in some cases they may strain the hands or wrists. They should be sparingly practised by those whose hand span is limited. Attain mastery with separate hands before playing the hands together.

ARPEGGIOS – BROKEN CHORDS

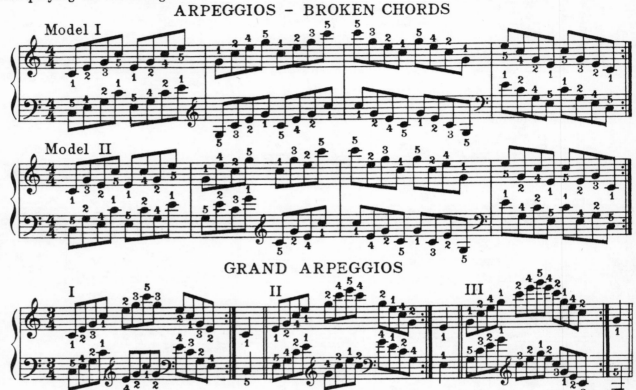

GRAND ARPEGGIOS

In passages that begin on a black key start with the second finger *(R.H.,*ascending, *L.H.,* descending) and play the thumb on the first white key.

MAJOR KEYS

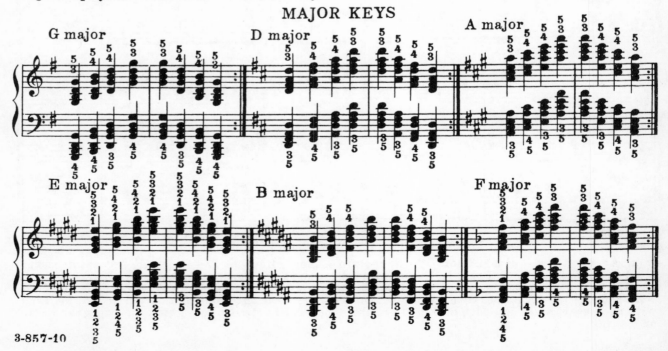

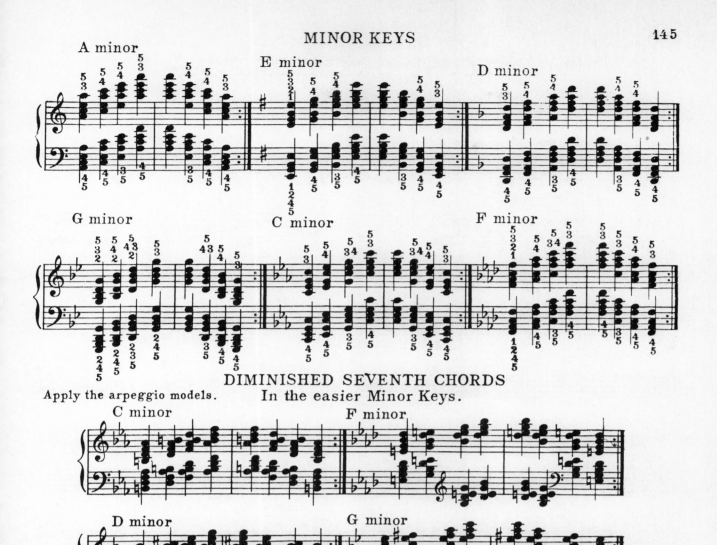

DIMINISHED SEVENTH CHORDS
In the easier Minor Keys.

Apply the arpeggio models.

DOMINANT SEVENTH CHORDS
In the easier Major and Minor Keys

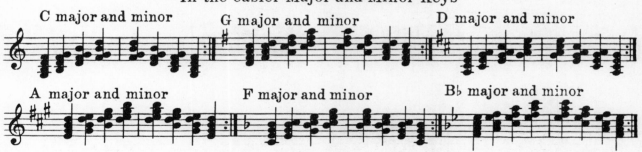

Crossing Fingers Over in Thirds.

The transposing of these exercises will prepare the hands for any Thirds that may occur in this Grade. Also practise the scales in staccato Thirds: 1-3, 1-3, 2-4, 2-4 and 3-5, 3-5; and in Staccato Sixths:1-5. This will afford excellent practice in wrist action.

SECOND GRADE STUDIES

KÖHLER, Op.157, № 3

Allegro comodo

For fluency in continuous five-finger figures, with alternating hands.

poco a poco cresc.

sempre cresc.

Practise slowly, with a firm even touch, at first. Eventually transpose to the neighboring major keys above and below original key.

Moderato

DUVERNOY, Op.176. № 4

For finger development in continuous broken triads.

Slowly, with precise finger stroke and lift, at first. Later transpose to D, E, A and easier keys.

STUDY
C MAJOR

LOUIS KÖHLER,
Op. 151, No 1

Moderato

STUDY
C MAJOR

LOUIS KÖHLER,
Op. 151, № 2

STUDY
C MAJOR

H. BERTINI

STUDY
D MAJOR

C. CZERNY,
Op. 139, № 42

Allegro comodo

STUDY
C MAJOR

A. LOESCHHORN,
Op. 65, № 4

Allegretto

II

STUDY
C MAJOR

H. BERENS,
Op. 70, № 34

Allegro moderato

STUDY

C. GURLITT
Op. 83, No 13.

For right-hand dexterity in three-finger figures

STUDY

C. GURLITT
Op. 83, No. 14.

For left-hand dexterity in three-finger figures.

156

Allegro

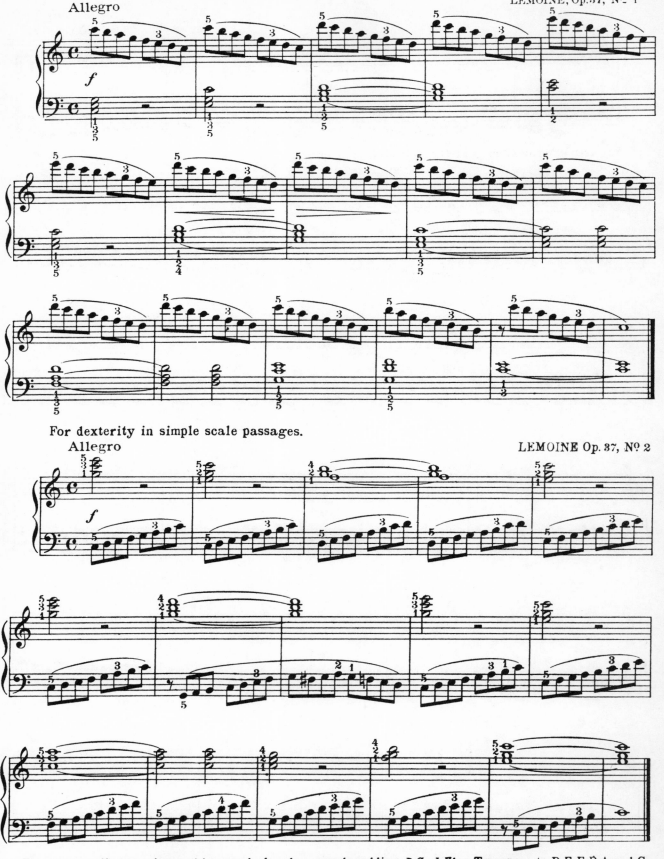

For dexterity in simple scale passages.

Allegro

LEMOINE Op. 37, No 2

These two studies may be combined and played as one, by adding *D.C. al Fine.* Transpose to D, E, F, B, A and G noting change in fingering: B maj. *L.H.*, F maj. *R.H.*, and reason therefor.

II

Allegro moderato

BURGMULLER, Op.100, № 21

For equality in broken triads, for alternating hands.

Coda

Piu lento

Play through twice before going to Coda. Later transpose to F and A, using same fingering.

STUDY

C. GURLITT
Op. 83, No 19.

Allegro vivace

Skill and endurance in finger passages for the right hand.

STUDY

C. GURLITT
Op.83, No 20.

Allegro vivace

For skill and endurance in finger passages for the left hand.

STUDY

F major

BERENS

Tempo di marcia

For finger passages and wrist action.

STUDY

C MAJOR

C. CZERNY,
Op. 777, Nº 21

II

STUDY
C MAJOR

H. BERENS,
Op. 70, № 44

Moderato *(gradually increase to Allegro)* KÖHLER, Op. 50, № 9

Development of force in continuous scale passages.

KÖHLER, Op. 50, № 10

The upper fingering is stronger for forte playing, and affords excellent practise. Practice both ways

ETUDE
C MAJOR

C. CZERNY
Op. 599, № 18

II

ETUDE

C MAJOR

C. CZERNY
Op. 139, № 61

Allegretto animato

Mixed technical forms: Triplets, arpeggios, chords, and scales.

Allegro moderato *(increase to Allegro)*

KÖHLER, Op.157, № 11

For dexterity in scale variants.

D.C. al Fine

Allegro moderato *(gradually increase to Allegro)*

DUVERNOY, Op.176, № 9

Practise hands separately at first. For fluency and equality in both hands.

Allegro moderato

LEMOINE, Op. 37, № 8

For fluency and dexterity in both hands, in Triplets.

(3 1) (3)

Coda

Slowly, with firm finger touch, until thoroughly learned, then increase speed. Later transpose.

For facility in scales and in broken Thirds.

BERENS, Op. 79, No. 19

For the chromatic scale and wrist action.

BERENS, Op. 79, No. 20

The previous study, with hands reversed.

Preceding studies should now be reviewed for increased velocity and general facility.

Allegro moderato

LEMOINE, Op. 37, № 20

For facility in continuous four-finger figures.

Fine

D.C. al Fine

a) Watch hand position and use fingers precisely and accurately in the contractions between 1st and 4th fingers.

11-736-24

174

CZERNY, Op.139-19

For fluency in scales, and wrist action in chords.

CZERNY, Op.139, № 45'

For melody with broken triad accompaniment.

Slowly and firmly at first, constantly reviewing until the study can be played up to time.

12-736-24

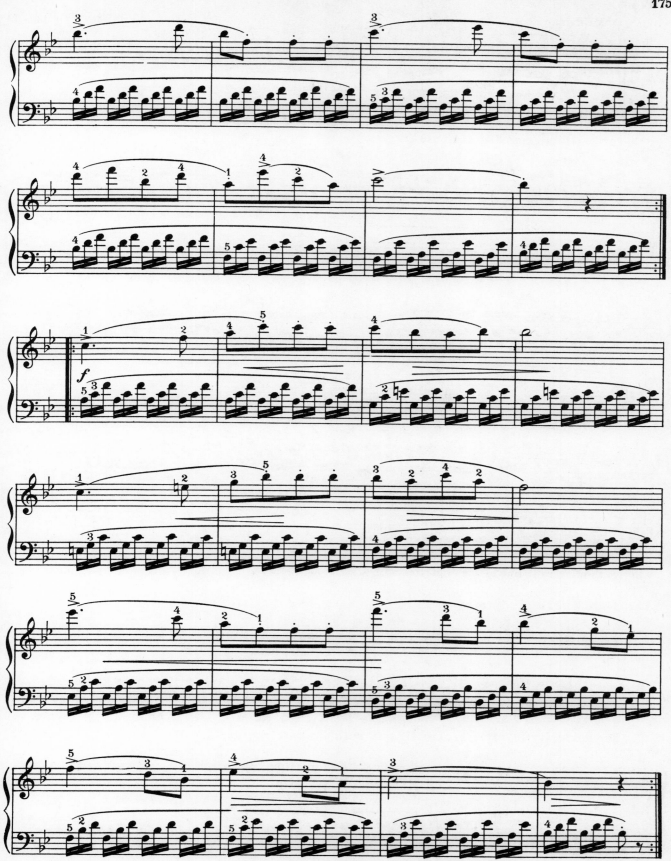

DÖRING Op.8. №1

Moderato

For skill in expanded diatonic figures.

Slowly, the fingers lifting high and playing with a firm, sure stroke.

Allegro moderato

For dexterity in rapid broken figures with staccato chords.

VELOCITY FIGURES

LOUIS KÖHLER, Op. 157. No. 8

See remarks - previous study.

Allegro giusto

(a)

For arpeggios and five-finger figures combined.

(a) Practise: Adagio *f* — Moderato *f* — Allegro *mf* — Allegro molto *p*

Later, transpose; adapting fingering.

15-736-24

STUDY

C. GURLITT
Op. 83, No 15.

For finger independence and velocity in broken chords for the right hand.

STUDY

C. GURLITT
Op.83, № 16.

For finger independence and velocity in broken chords for the left hand.

Independence and security in broken chords for the right hand.

Pay strict attention to fingers; precise and firm stroke, quick lift and control at a slow tempo. Transpose to easy keys.

Moderato

KÖHLER, Op. 50. N? 4

Independence and security in broken chords for the left hand.

For dexterity in Trills and five-finger figures.

Observe previous remarks and suggestions.

LOESCHHORN, Op. 66-8

Moderato

P dolce ed espressivo

Facility in continuous broken triad variant.

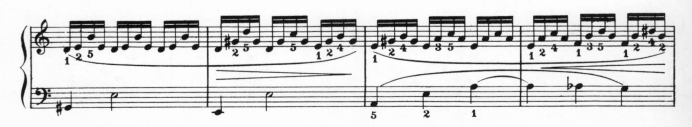

STUDY

CZERNY, Op. 139. Nº 24

For extended scale passages and broken chords.

Allegro vivace

CZERNY, Op. 821, Nº 22

For skill in embellished broken triads.

Allegretto vivo ♩. = 80

KÖHLER, Op. 242. № 10

For facility and equality in broken Thirds.

SCHUMANN, Op. 68. № 14

Allegro moderato

For dexterity and smoothness in arpeggio figures for alternating hands.

Facility and tone shading in chromatic scales and wrist action.

Allegro

Practise very slowly and firmly until the fingers are absolutely sure of the notes.

DUVERNOY, Op. 120, No. 7

Moderato

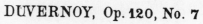

For rapid thumb and second finger passing and use of first and second endings.

Dom. 7th of G

Dom. 7th of C

cres.

Name this chord.

cres.

7-857-10

STUDY

DUVERNOY

For double note playing and the use of the damper pedal.

ETUDE

DUVERNOY

For dexterity in wrist staccato.

Allegro grazioso

BERENS, Op. 79, No. 16

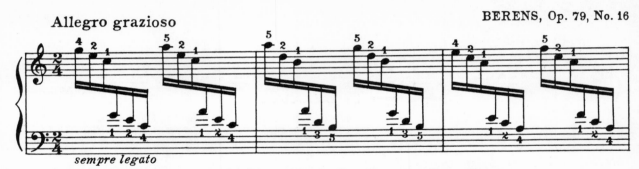

sempre legato

Arpeggio figures in alternating hands. Play with rippling fluency and smoothness.

Allegretto con grazia

BERENS, Op. 79, No. 15

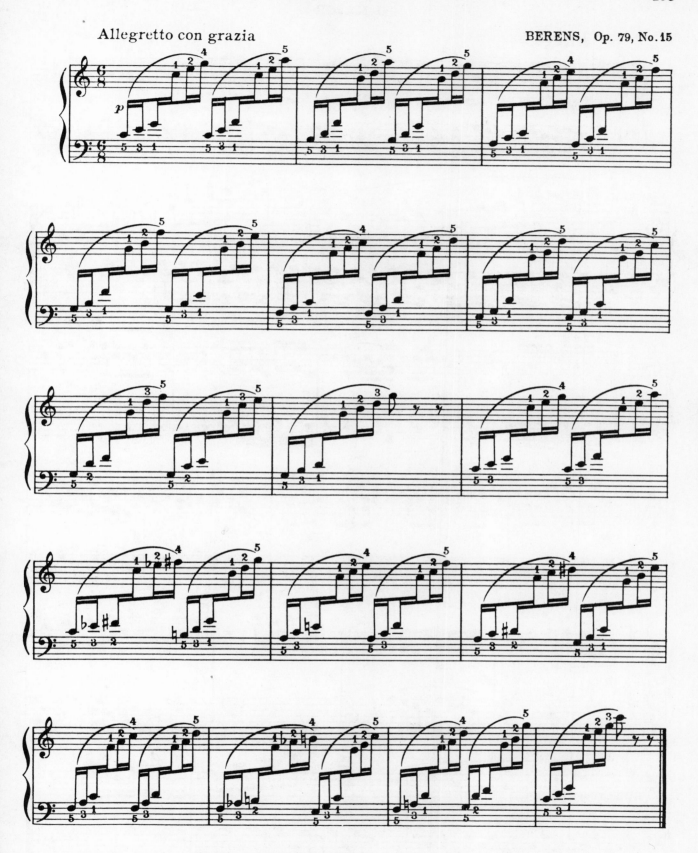

STUDY
G MAJOR

C. CZERNY,
Op. 139, № 25

STUDY
F MAJOR

C. CZERNY
Op. 777, № 20

II

ETUDE
F MAJOR

C. CZERNY
Op. 599, № 87

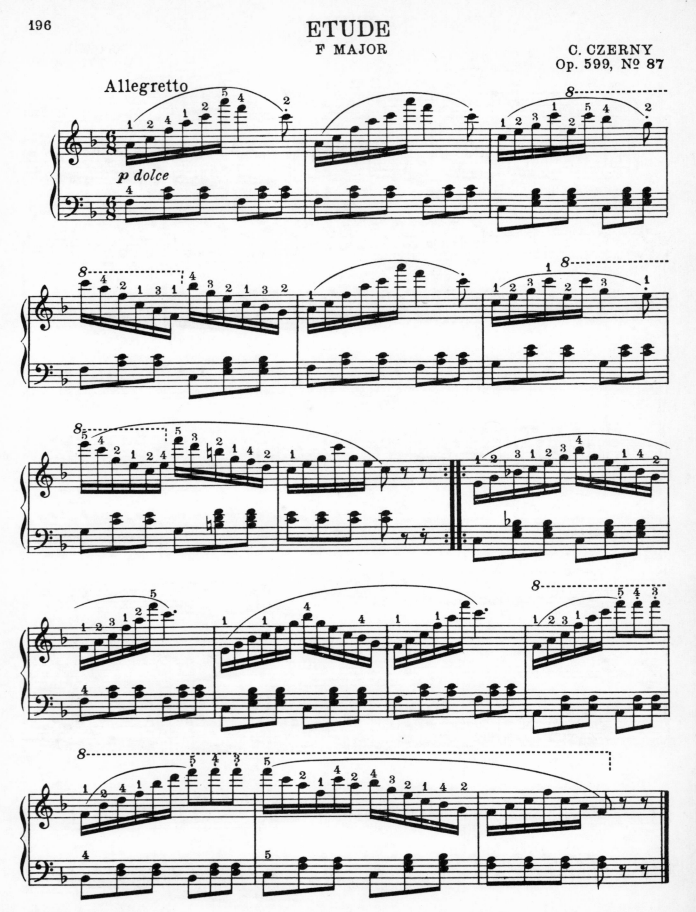

ETUDE
G MAJOR

C. CZERNY
Op. 599, № 59

STUDY

CZERNY

Moderato

p

For developing a finger staccato touch.

simile

f

p

f

mp

sempre staccato

THE SPINNING WHEEL

A. LOESCHHORN
Op. 65, No.46

Allegro vivo

Rapid scale and four-finger passages, with triads.

TO CODA

Coda

F 3

D. C. al ⊕ e poi la Coda

ALLEGRETTO

CLEMENTI
Op. 36

Allegretto

PRELUDE

Allegro moderato

HENRY J. BERTINI
Op. 100, No. 3.

Fine

MARCH

Tempo di marcia

CZERNY

ETUDE JOYEUSE

LOUIS KOHLER

ETUDE

CZERNY

ON THE TRAIN

HELLER